# Diagnose & Prescribe

## Diagnostic Tests
### for Middle Grades
### Social Studies Skills

Needham, Massachusetts
Upper Saddle River, New Jersey
Glenview, Illinois

ISBN 0-13-067784-1

3 4 5 6 7 8 9 10    06 05 04 03 02

# TABLE OF CONTENTS

*Diagnostic Tests for Middle Grades Social Studies Skills* is part of the Prentice Hall Assessment Systems, which provides comprehensive support for both program content assessment and preparation for high-stakes standardized tests. This booklet will help you evaluate whether students have mastered the social studies skills they will need to successfully answer test questions on content. *Diagnostic Tests for Middle Grades Social Studies Skills* consists of four sets of tests that focus on geographic literacy, visual analysis, communications, and critical thinking and reading. Each set of tests consists of Test A and Test B.

The **Geography Literacy Tests** will help you evaluate student facility in:
• Using the Cartographer's Tools
• Using Special Purpose Maps

The **Visual Analysis Tests** will help you evaluate student facility in:
• Analyzing Graphic Data
• Analyzing Images

The **Communications Tests** will help you evaluate student facility in:
• Using Reliable Information
• Transferring Information from One Medium to Another
• Synthesizing Information
• Supporting a Position

The **Critical Thinking and Reading Tests** will help you evaluate student facility in:
• Identifying Main Ideas/Summarizing
• Sequencing
• Identifying Cause and Effect/Making Predictions
• Drawing Inferences and Conclusions
• Making Valid Generalizations
• Distinguishing Fact and Opinion
• Comparing and Contrasting

• Analyzing Primary Sources
• Recognizing Bias and Propaganda
• Identifying Frame of Reference and Point of View
• Decision-making
• Problem-solving

## How to Use the Diagnostic Tests

Use the skills-specific diagnostic multiple-choice tests to help you identify areas in which individual students are having difficulty. Each question is correlated to one of the skills listed above.

Use students' test results to help pinpoint the skills your students have mastered and the skills your students need to practice. Then use the **Correlations to Program Resources** starting on page 38 to prescribe skills practice and reinforcement in the areas your students need to gain proficiency. Find your textbook program in the Correlations to Program Resources. Then locate skills practice and reinforcement in the Student Edition, Teacher's Edition, and Teaching Resources. Have your students use these resources to help them develop proficiency in the social studies skills they need to succeed on tests.

## When to Use the Diagnostic Tests

Each set of tests includes Test A and a Test B. Use Test A at the beginning of the year to evaluate students' proficiency in social studies skills. During the course of the year, administer Test B to measure students' progress. You may wish to give Test B long before a high-stakes test is administered to allow students to time to develop proficiency at the skills they will need to answer test questions successfully.

# TEST A — GEOGRAPHIC LITERACY

**Directions:** *Use the map below to answer questions 1–3.*

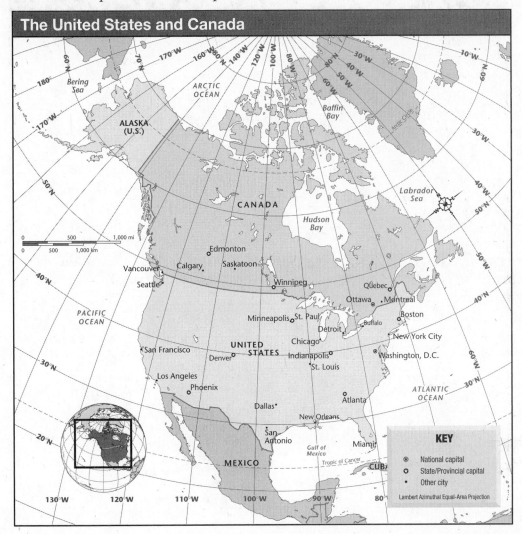

The United States and Canada

**1.** At what latitude and longitude is the city of New Orleans located?

   **A** 40°N, 100°W
   **B** 40°N, 80°W
   **C** 30°N, 90°W
   **D** 30°N, 100°W

**2.** Which of the following statements *best* describes the relative location of New Orleans?

   **A** It is southwest of Atlanta.
   **B** It is north of Denver.
   **C** It is southwest of Baltimore.
   **D** It is northeast of Washington, D.C.

**3.** Which of the following statements *best* describes the approximate distance between Chicago and Washington, D.C.?

   **A** The distance is approximately 2,000 kilometers.
   **B** The distance is approximately 1,000 kilometers.
   **C** The distance is approximately 50 kilometers.
   **D** The distance is just over 150 kilometers.

GO ON

## T E S T  A — GEOGRAPHIC LITERACY (*continued*)

**Directions:** *Use the map below to answer questions 4–7.*

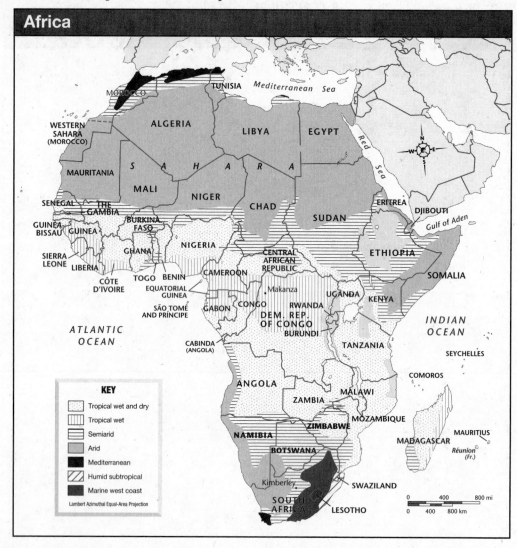

Africa

**KEY**

- Tropical wet and dry
- Tropical wet
- Semiarid
- Arid
- Mediterranean
- Humid subtropical
- Marine west coast

Lambert Azimuthal Equal-Area Projection

4. What two climate zones appear *most widely* throughout northern Africa?

   **A** tropical wet and tropical wet and dry
   **B** tropical wet and arid
   **C** arid and semiarid
   **D** semiarid and Mediterranean

5. According to the map, which of the following statements is true about Botswana?

   **A** The Tropic of Capricorn passes through it.
   **B** Most of the region has an arid climate.
   **C** It is located west of South Africa.
   **D** It has a tropical wet and dry climate.

6. Arid land in Africa is usually bordered by

   **A** humid subtropical regions.
   **B** marine west coast regions.
   **C** semiarid regions.
   **D** tropical wet regions.

7. Which of the following cross the continent of Africa?
   1. Equator
   2. Tropic of Cancer
   3. Tropic of Capricorn

   **A** 1 and 2 only     **C** 1 and 3 only
   **B** 1, 2, and 3       **D** 2 and 3 only

GO ON

Name _____  Date _____  Class _____

**T E S T  A — GEOGRAPHIC LITERACY** *(continued)*

**Directions:**  *Use the map below to answer questions 8–11.*

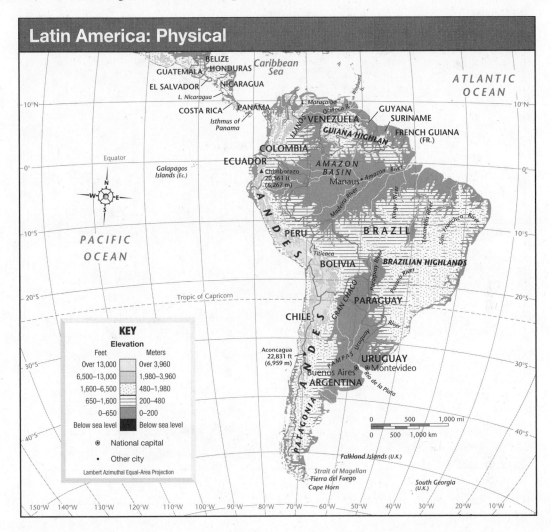

**Latin America: Physical**

8. What type of information is shown in the key for the map of Central and South America?

   **A** natural vegetation, mountain ranges, and physical features

   **B** climatic regions, mountain ranges, and volcanoes

   **C** elevation, national capitals, and other cities

   **D** population density, wind currents, and geological features

9. In which country is 10°S, 50°W located?

   **A** Brazil          **C** Peru

   **B** Paraguay      **D** Argentina

10. According to the map, which of the following areas has the highest elevation?

    **A** the Brazilian Highlands

    **B** the Andes Mountains

    **C** the Guiana Highlands

    **D** Patagonia

11. Which of the following bodies of water is located east of the Caribbean Sea?

    **A** the Atlantic Ocean

    **B** the Gulf of Mexico

    **C** the Panama Canal

    **D** the Pacific Ocean

GO ON

Diagnostic Tests                                    7

Name _____ Date _____ Class _____

***Directions:*** *Use the map below to answer questions 12–16.*

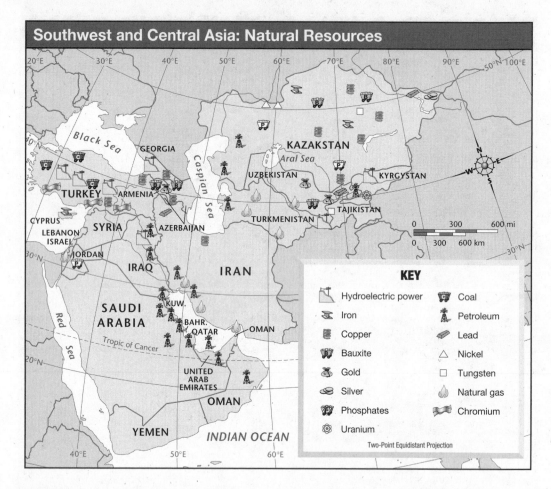

**12.** Which of the following natural resource is found in Saudi Arabia?

   **A** silver       **C** petroleum
   **B** coal         **D** iron

**13.** What natural resource is located immediately east of the Caspian Sea?

   **A** bauxite      **C** petroleum
   **B** nickel       **D** coal

**14.** Where are *most* of the petroleum resources located in Iran and Saudi Arabia?

   **A** on their eastern borders
   **B** near the coast
   **C** on the Indian Ocean
   **D** near their border with Kyrgystan

**15.** According to the map, petroleum is the only natural resource found in

   **A** Oman.       **C** Turkey.
   **B** Iran.        **D** Iraq.

**16.** Which of the following statements *best* describes the location of iron deposits nearest to the Aral Sea?

   **A** Iron deposits are found northwest of the Aral Sea.
   **B** Iron deposits are found east of the Aral Sea.
   **C** Iron deposits are found northeast of the Aral Sea.
   **D** Iron deposits are found southeast of the Aral Sea.

Name _____  Date _____  Class _____

**Directions:** *Use the diagram below to answer questions 1–4.*

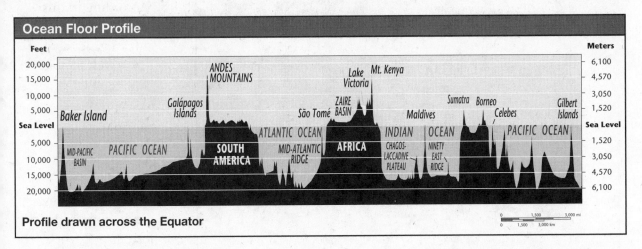

Ocean Floor Profile

Profile drawn across the Equator

1. What area of the world is shown on this map?

    A  the ocean floor below South America and Africa
    B  the ocean floor below all of Earth
    C  the ocean floor along the Equator
    D  the ocean floor along the eastern hemisphere of Earth

2. According to this diagram, what do Baker Island, the Galápagos Islands, and the Maldives have in common?

    A  They are below sea level.
    B  They are at sea level.
    C  They are in the Pacific Ocean.
    D  They are surrounded by land.

3. On this profile of the ocean floor, where are the lowest points on Earth located?

    A  in the Pacific Ocean
    B  in the Indian Ocean
    C  on the coast of South America
    D  in the Atlantic Ocean

4. Based on the information in the diagram, which of the following is a true statement?

    A  Mt. Kenya is the highest point on the South American continent.
    B  Celebes and Borneo are higher than Sumatra.
    C  Most of South America is at or near sea level, and most of Africa is above sea level.
    D  Lake Victoria is located at sea level.

GO ON

Name _____ Date _____ Class _____

# T E S T  B — GEOGRAPHIC LITERACY (continued)

**Directions:** *Use the map below to answer questions 5–9.*

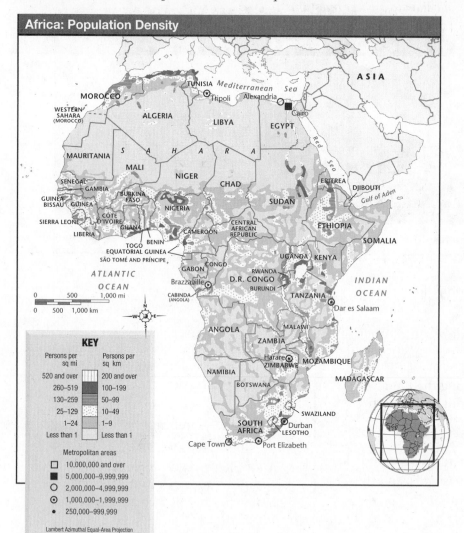

Africa: Population Density

5. According to this map, what area of Africa generally has the fewest people per square mile?

   A central
   B north
   C south
   D southwest

6. About how many people live in the city of Cairo, Egypt?

   A between 2,000,000 and 4,999,999
   B less than 1 person per square mile
   C between 5,000,000 and 9,999,999
   D 10,000,000 or more

7. What is the approximate distance between Cape Town, South Africa, and Harare, Zimbabwe?

   A about 1,400 miles
   B about 1,000 miles
   C about 1,200 miles
   D about 2,000 miles

8. Which of the following cities has the highest population?

   A Tripoli, Libya.
   B Alexandria, Egypt.
   C Cairo, Egypt.
   D Dar es Salaam, Tanzania.

9. Using this map, what is one thing the South African cities of Cape Town, Port Elizabeth, and Durban have in common?

   A They are in areas with 10 to 49 people per square mile.
   B They are located on Africa's western coast.
   C They are located on Africa's southern coast.
   D Their populations are 10,000,000 and over.

GO ON

Name _____ Date _____ Class _____

# TEST B — GEOGRAPHIC LITERACY *(continued)*

**Directions:** *Use the map below to answer questions 10–13.*

**Western Europe: Political**

**KEY**

— National boundary
⊛ National capital
• Other city

Lambert Azimuthal Equal-Area Projection

**10.** What is the capital city of Italy?

   **A** Rome        **C** Naples

   **B** Milan        **D** Paris

**11.** Which of the following cities is the closest in distance to Vienna, Austria?

   **A** Lisbon       **C** Athens

   **B** Helsinki     **D** Dublin

**12.** Which country is located west of Spain?

   **A** Portugal          **C** Finland

   **B** United Kingdom   **D** Italy

**13.** Which body of water separates the United Kingdom and France?

   **A** Bay of Biscay

   **B** English Channel

   **C** North Sea

   **D** Mediterranean Sea

**TEST B — GEOGRAPHIC LITERACY** (continued)

*Directions:* Use the map below to answer questions 14–17.

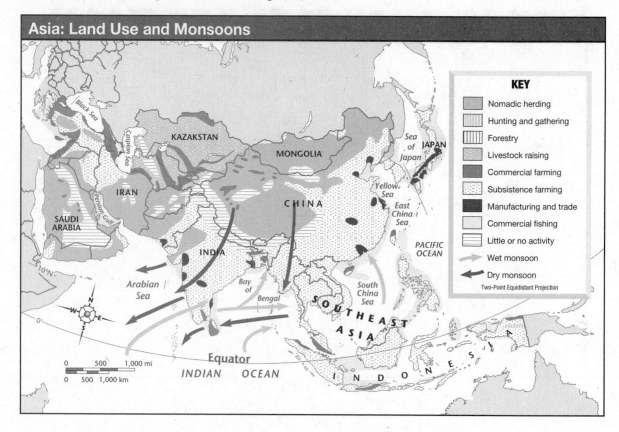

**Asia: Land Use and Monsoons**

KEY
- Nomadic herding
- Hunting and gathering
- Forestry
- Livestock raising
- Commercial farming
- Subsistence farming
- Manufacturing and trade
- Commercial fishing
- Little or no activity
- Wet monsoon
- Dry monsoon

Two-Point Equidistant Projection

**14.** For which of the following activities is the majority of the land in India used?

  **A** nomadic herding
  **B** subsistence farming
  **C** manufacturing and trade
  **D** commercial farming

**15.** In which direction do the dry monsoons tend to move?

  **A** to the northwest
  **B** to the northeast
  **C** to the southeast
  **D** to the southwest

**16.** Which Asian country lies along the equator?

  **A** China        **C** Indonesia
  **B** India        **D** Saudi Arabia

**17.** For what purpose is *most* of the land in Kazakstan used?

  **A** livestock raising
  **B** commercial farming
  **C** subsistence farming
  **D** commercial fishing

Name _____ Date _____ Class _____

**Directions:** *Study the diagram of sections and townships. Then answer questions 1–4.*

The Land Ordinance of 1785 set up a system for surveying and settling the Northwest Territory. The Land Ordinance of 1785 divided the land into townships that consist of 36 sections.

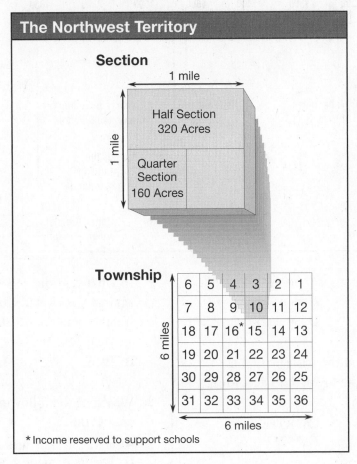

**The Northwest Territory**

**Section**

1 mile

1 mile

Half Section
320 Acres

Quarter Section
160 Acres

**Township**

6 miles

| 6 | 5 | 4 | 3 | 2 | 1 |
| 7 | 8 | 9 | 10 | 11 | 12 |
| 18 | 17 | 16* | 15 | 14 | 13 |
| 19 | 20 | 21 | 22 | 23 | 24 |
| 30 | 29 | 28 | 27 | 26 | 25 |
| 31 | 32 | 33 | 34 | 35 | 36 |

6 miles

* Income reserved to support schools

**1.** According to the diagram, how many square miles are in each section?

**A** 6 square miles
**B** 1 square mile
**C** 36 square miles
**D** 1/4 square mile

**2.** How many acres are in each half section?

**A** 320 acres    **C** 1 acre
**B** 160 acres    **D** 36 acres

**3.** How many square miles are in each township?

**A** 6 square miles    **C** 36 square miles
**B** 12 square miles    **D** 360 square miles

**4.** How many sections in a township are reserved to support schools?

**A** 10 sections    **C** 2 sections
**B** 6 sections    **D** 1 section

GO ON

**T E S T   A — VISUAL ANALYSIS** *(continued)*

*Directions:* Use the time line below to answer questions 5–9.

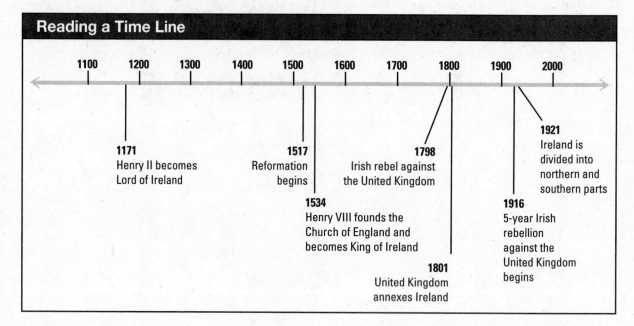

**Reading a Time Line**

1171 — Henry II becomes Lord of Ireland
1517 — Reformation begins
1534 — Henry VIII founds the Church of England and becomes King of Ireland
1798 — Irish rebel against the United Kingdom
1801 — United Kingdom annexes Ireland
1916 — 5-year Irish rebellion against the United Kingdom begins
1921 — Ireland is divided into northern and southern parts

**5.** Into what intervals is the time line divided?

   **A** 1,000 years      **C** 500 years
   **B** 100 years        **D** 50 years

**6.** In what year did the Irish *first* rebel against the United Kingdom according to the time line?

   **A** 1517      **C** 1800
   **B** 1798      **D** 1921

**7.** Which of the following events occurred *before* the founding of the Church of England by Henry VIII?

   **A** Ireland is divided into northern and southern parts.
   **B** United Kingdom annexes Ireland.
   **C** Henry VIII becomes King of Ireland.
   **D** Henry II becomes Lord of Ireland.

**8.** In what year did the 5-year Irish rebellion against the United Kingdom end, with Ireland being divided into two parts?

   **A** 1900      **C** 1921
   **B** 1916      **D** 1925

**9.** Which of the following events occurred *after* 1700?

   **A** Henry II becomes Lord of Ireland.
   **B** The Reformation begins.
   **C** Henry VIII founds the Church of England.
   **D** United Kingdom annexes Ireland.

STOP

Name _____  Date _____  Class _____

# TEST B — VISUAL ANALYSIS

*Directions:* Use the time line below to answer questions 1–5.

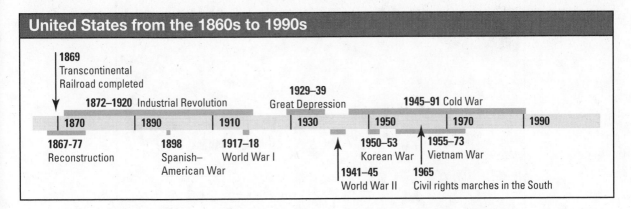

**United States from the 1860s to 1990s**

1869 Transcontinental Railroad completed

1872–1920 Industrial Revolution

1929–39 Great Depression

1945–91 Cold War

1870  1890  1910  1930  1950  1970  1990

1867-77 Reconstruction

1898 Spanish–American War

1917–18 World War I

1950–53 Korean War

1955–73 Vietnam War

1941–45 World War II

1965 Civil rights marches in the South

1. According to the time line which sequence of events is correct?

   A Spanish–American War; Industrial Revolution; World War II; Great Depression
   B Reconstruction; Great Depression; Korean War; Vietnam War
   C Great Depression; World War I; Cold War; Industrial Revolution
   D World War I; World War II; Great Depression; Korean War

2. Which of the following statements is true, based on the information in the time line?

   A Between 1910 and 1970, the United States experienced six wars.
   B The end of the Great Depression was marked by the beginning of World War I.
   C At the end of World War I, the Industrial Revolution had nearly ended.
   D The Korean War and the Vietnam War overlapped by two years.

3. Which of the following events occurred during the Cold War?

   A World War II
   B the Great Depression
   C the Vietnam War
   D the Industrial Revolution

4. During which of the following periods did civil rights marches in the South occur?

   A Reconstruction
   B World War I
   C the Great Depression
   D the Cold War

5. Which event on the time line spans the *greatest* amount of time?

   A Great Depression
   B Transcontinental Railroad completed
   C Industrial Revolution
   D Korean War

GO ON

Name _____ Date _____ Class _____

*Directions:* *Examine the cartoon below, and answer questions 6–10.*

**6.** Who or what do the people in the water represent?

   **A** They represent people who have jumped in before knowing how to swim.

   **B** They represent Russians invading U.S. shorelines.

   **C** They represent immigrants coming to the United States.

   **D** They represent big business in America.

**7.** Who or what does the lifeguard represent?

   **A** He represents the European Union.

   **B** He represents the United States Coast Guard.

   **C** He represents American immigrants.

   **D** He represents the United States government.

**8.** Which of the following would be the *best* caption for this cartoon?

   **A** "Who taught these people how to speak English?"

   **B** "Uncle Sam realizes he can't swim."

   **C** "Can America save everyone?"

   **D** "The war against terrorism comes to America's shores."

**9.** Which of the following scenes presents the message *most* similar to the one depicted in the cartoon?

   **A** A woman dressed as the Statue of Liberty looks sadly at a long line of children carrying empty bowls as she ladles the last of her pot of oatmeal to the first child in line.

   **B** The President of the United States shakes hands with the president of another nation.

   **C** An older man and woman sit on a park bench smiling and laughing as they toss bread to a flock of hungry pigeons.

   **D** A well-dressed man and woman look away as they walk past a long line of homeless people begging for money.

**10.** Which of the following statements *best* explains the symbolism in this cartoon?

   **A** The umbrella is a symbol that represents the sky.

   **B** The chair is a symbol that represents big business.

   **C** The word "Help" is a symbol that represents English-speaking immigrants.

   **D** The life preserver is a symbol that represents American aid.

Name _____  Date _____  Class _____

*Directions:* Read the following passage. Then answer questions 1–4.

> "From this the question arises whether it is better to be loved more than feared, or feared more than loved. The reply is, that one ought to be both feared and loved, but as it is difficult for the two to go together, it is much safer to be feared than loved . . . for it may be said of men in general that they are ungrateful, . . . anxious to avoid danger, and greedy. . . . Men find it easier to attack one who makes himself loved than one who makes himself feared. . . .
>
> A prince . . . must imitate the fox and the lion, for the lion cannot protect himself from traps, and the fox cannot defend himself from wolves. One must therefore be a fox to recognize traps, and a lion to frighten wolves. . . . Therefore, a wise ruler ought not keep his word when by so doing it would be against his interest. . . . If men were all good, this [rule] would not be a good one; but as they are bad, and would not be honest with you, so you are not bound to keep your word with them. . . ."
>
> —Niccoló Machiavelli, *The Prince* (1513)

1. Which of the following does Machiavelli contrast in this passage?

   **A** a fox and a lion
   **B** a fox and a wolf
   **C** a wolf and a lion
   **D** a lion and a wise ruler

2. Machiavelli would *most likely* disagree with which of the following statements?

   **A** Men are mostly bad.
   **B** A prince is responsible for keeping his word.
   **C** A prince cannot survive without both intelligence and strength.
   **D** A feared ruler is a powerful ruler.

3. To which category do the following belong?
   • Men are greedy.
   • Men are ungrateful.
   • Men are anxious to avoid danger.

   **A** reasons it is safer to be loved than feared
   **B** reasons to imitate a lion
   **C** reasons to imitate a wolf
   **D** reasons it is safer to be feared than loved

4. Which of the following *best* describes a "Machiavellian" leader?

   **A** one who rejects morality in order to pursue political gains
   **B** one who guarantees that his or her subjects are fairly treated
   **C** one who has feelings of inferiority
   **D** one who expects all people to be fair and honest

## T E S T  A — CRITICAL THINKING AND READING (continued)

*Directions:* *Read the following passage. Then answer questions 5–7.*

---

*The Sirens: A Greek Myth From the Adventures of Ulysses,* retold by Bernard Evslin

"In the first light of morning Ulysses awoke and called his crew about him.

'Men,' he said. 'Listen well, for your lives today hang upon what I am about to tell you. That large island to the west is Thrinacia, where we must make a landfall, for our provisions run low. But to get to the island we must pass through a narrow strait. And at the head of this strait is a rocky islet where dwell two sisters called Sirens, whose voices you must not hear. Now I shall guard you against their singing, which would lure you to shipwreck, but first you must bind me to the mast. Tie me tightly, as though I were a dangerous captive. And no matter how I struggle, no matter what signals I make to you, do not release me, lest I follow their voices to destruction, taking you with me.'

Thereupon Ulysses took a large lump of the beeswax . . . and kneaded it in his powerful hands until it became soft. Then he went to each man of the crew and plugged his ears with soft wax; he caulked their ears so tightly that they could hear nothing but the thin pulsing of their own blood. . . .

Ulysses had left his own ears unplugged because he had to remain in command of the ship and had need of his hearing. Every sound means something upon the sea. But when they drew near the rocky islet and he heard the first faint strains of the Sirens' singing, then he wished he, too, had stopped his own ears with wax. All his strength suddenly surged toward the sound of those magical voices. The very hair of his head seemed to be tugging at his scalp, trying to fly away. His eyeballs started out of his head."

---

**5.** Put the following events in the sequence in which they would have occurred on Ulysses's ship.
1. Tie Ulysses to the mast.
2. Pass through a narrow strait.
3. Reach Thrinacia.
4. Put wax in your ears.

**A** 4, 1, 2, 3     **C** 2, 1, 3, 4
**B** 4, 1, 3, 4     **D** 1, 4, 2, 3

**6.** What would be the *most likely* effect if the crew released Ulysses?

**A** The Sirens would board the ship and take control.
**B** The Sirens would regain their status as captains of the ship.
**C** Ulysses and his crew would die because Ulysses would follow the Sirens' voices and lead the crew to shipwreck.
**D** Ulysses would drown before he has a chance to hear the Sirens sing.

**7.** Which statement *best* describes the fate of other ships and crews who had tried to reach the island?

**A** The ships were boarded by the Sirens, and the crews were taken prisoner.
**B** The ships turned around, and the crews returned home.
**C** The ships were captured by the Sirens, and the crews were drowned.
**D** The Sirens' voices lured the crews to steer toward the rocks, the ships were destroyed, and the crews were killed.

>GO ON>

**TEST A — CRITICAL THINKING AND READING** (*continued*)

**Directions:** *Read the passage below. Then answer questions 8 and 9.*

> In 1989, communism in Poland ended, and Poland adopted the free enterprise system. In this kind of system, people can open and run their own businesses free from government control. The fall of communism meant that the government no longer controlled the creation of jobs. As a result, many government jobs disappeared. The loss of jobs forced people to look for jobs elsewhere. Because of free enterprise, small companies now have the freedom to grow naturally. Growing companies have created new and better jobs for some people, but other people remain jobless.

**8.** What is the main idea of this passage?

  **A** Following communism, the free enterprise system was adopted in Poland, and although many government jobs were eliminated, privately owned businesses created new and better jobs.

  **B** When communism ended in Poland, government businesses thrived despite the elimination of many government jobs.

  **C** After communism ended in Poland, private industry grew because people did not want government jobs any longer.

  **D** Growing companies in Poland following the fall of communism allowed the country to become a global economic power.

**9.** Which of the following statements would *most likely* be supported by a member of the Communist party?

  **A** When communism ended, Poland adopted the free enterprise system so that businesses would not be government-controlled.

  **B** The free enterprise system created many new and better jobs.

  **C** Many small companies were formed as a result of the free enterprise system.

  **D** Poland's economy suffered when communism ended, and people lost their jobs.

**Directions:** *Read the following passage. Then answer questions 10 and 11.*

> "My friends . . . when you deposit money in a bank, the bank does not put the money into a safe deposit vault. It invests your money, puts it to work. . . . [Why did banks go out of business?] There was a general rush so great that the soundest banks could not get enough currency to meet the demand. . . . [Then he described the plan to gradually reopen banks.] There is no occasion for worry. . . . When people find they can get their money, the phantom of fear will soon be laid [to rest]. I can assure you that it is safer to keep your money in a reopened bank than under the mattress."
> —President Franklin D. Roosevelt, in a radio "fireside chat" (1933)

**10.** Which of the following statements is an opinion?

  **A** When people find they can get their money, the phantom of fear will soon be laid to rest.

  **B** Banks could not get enough currency to meet people's demands.

  **C** Some people kept their money under mattresses instead of in a bank.

  **D** Deposited money is invested by the bank.

**11.** With which of the following statements would a banker probably disagree?

  **A** Banks are the safest places to keep money.

  **B** Investing deposited money is an irresponsible function of a bank.

  **C** The responsibility of a bank is to use deposited money wisely.

  **D** People who deposit their money in a bank will not worry as much about their money.

**T E S T  A — CRITICAL THINKING AND READING** *(continued)*

*Directions:* *Read the following passage. Then answer questions 12–14.*

> "This is the country for a man to enjoy himself: Ohio, Indiana, and the Missouri Territory. . . .
>
> There is enough to spare of everything a person can desire; [I] have not heard either man or woman speak a word against the government or the price of [food and other supplies].
>
> The poorest families adorn [decorate] the table three times a day like a wedding dinner. . . . Say, is it so in England?
>
> If you knew the difference between this country and England you would need no persuading to leave it and come hither [here]."
>
> —Samuel Crabtree, in a letter to his brother in England about what he found after arriving in the United States (1818)

**12.** Which of the following two things in America does Samuel Crabtree contrast with those in England in this passage?

 **A** man or woman and the government
 **B** people's opinions of the government and the resources available to them
 **C** poor families and a wedding dinner
 **D** the price of food and supplies

**13.** What is the purpose of Samuel Crabtree's letter?

 **A** to plead with his brother to rescue him from the hardships in America
 **B** to describe his unhappiness with life in America
 **C** to persuade his brother to move to America
 **D** to describe how the poorest families lived

**14.** How does Samuel Crabtree's letter show his pride in his country?

 **A** He is proud that he does not have contact with England.
 **B** He explains that, although he has not heard people speak against the government, he thinks they are unhappy with the price of food.
 **C** He doesn't understand how the poor can eat three times a day.
 **D** His letter shows the economic opportunity that Americans enjoyed.

---

*Directions:* *Read the following passage. Then answer question 15.*

Officials of a major city in the United States are developing plans to build a new mass transit system that would replace the current outdated system. The officials are concerned with correcting several major problems that exist in the current system such as, increasing the number of passengers the system can accommodate and decreasing long delays during peak traffic times. Also, the current route does not travel to areas of new business development in the downtown area, its tracks have caused a major highway to be redirected, and the system has been known to malfunction during the city's harsh winters.

**15.** Which of the following would *not* address a concern of the officials as they work to develop a new mass transit system?

 **A** updating the location of stations throughout the city
 **B** providing additional seating capacity
 **C** designing new routes that allow traffic to pass more freely through the city
 **D** installing automated ticket machines at each station

20

# TEST A — CRITICAL THINKING AND READING *(continued)*

*Directions:* *Read the following passage. Then answer questions 16–18.*

> "With this lodging and diet, our extreme [work] in bearing and planting [stockade walls] . . . strained and bruised us, and our continual labor in the [extreme] heat . . . weakened us. . . .
>
> From May to September, [we] . . . lived upon [fish], and sea crabs. Fifty in this time we buried. . . .
>
> But now all our [food was gone], the [fish] gone, all helps abandoned, [and] each hour [we expected] the fury of the [natives]. . . . God, the patron of all good [efforts]. . . so changed the hearts of the [natives] that they brought such plenty of their fruits and provision as no man wanted."
>
> —John Smith, describing the "starving time" of Jamestown colony in 1607, from the *General History of Virginia* (1624)

**16.** You are one of the Jamestown colonists who was starving in 1607, and the Indians have not brought food for you to eat. You attend a colony meeting. Which of the following suggestions would you reject as you work to find a solution to your hunger?

**A** Some of the men should leave the colony to hunt for food.

**B** The colony should work toward peaceful relations with the Indians and ask them to teach the colonists how to survive.

**C** The colonists should barter with the Indians for food.

**D** The colonists should wait for supplies to come from England.

**17.** To what was John Smith referring when he wrote "Fifty in this time we buried. . . ."

**A** colonists     **C** fish
**B** Native Americans   **D** crabs

**18.** Which of the following *best* explains why John Smith attributes the Indians' good will toward the colonists to God?

**A** The Indians did not want to fight with the colonists anymore.

**B** The colonists believed that God was the creator of all good things.

**C** God helped the Indians see that the colonists needed help as a reward to the colonists for their hard work.

**D** Some colonists were unhappy that their survival was a result of the Indians' help.

## T E S T  A — CRITICAL THINKING AND READING (*continued*)

**Directions:** *Read the passage below. Then answer the question that follows.*

> "The first reason why we [left] Russia, it is because we would like to have freedom. . . .
>
> I have freedom here. I can see here not propaganda movies, not propaganda plays, not propaganda literature. I can talk with different people. If I want, I can move [to] another city, [to] another country. Maybe I [won't] go to another country, but I know absolutely exactly that [it] is possible."
>
> —Yuri Sinelnikov, describing why he and his wife left the Soviet Union to come to the United States, in an interview (1970s)

**19.** Which of the following *best* describes the viewpoint of Yuri Sinelnikov toward America?

   **A** He understands that he can move to another country.
   **B** He recognizes and appreciates the freedoms of the United States.
   **C** He is bitter toward Russia because of the propaganda that he was forced to watch and read while he lived there.
   **D** He values the propaganda that he read and watched while living in Russia.

**Directions:** *Read the passages below. Then answer the question that follows.*

> **A Cherokee woman, urging resistance to the United States government plan to move their people west, in a petition (1818):**
>
> We have heard with painful feelings that the bounds of the land we now possess are to be drawn into very narrow limits. The land was given to us by the Great Spirit above as our common right, to raise our children upon. . . . We, therefore, humbly petition . . . the head men of warriors, to hold out to the last in support of our common rights, as the Cherokee nations have been the first settlers of the land. . . . [We] claim the right of the soil.
>
> **John Louis O'Sullivan, describing the nation's destiny to grow, in an editorial in the New York Morning News (1845):**
>
> Our manifest destiny [is] to overspread and to possess the whole of the continent which [God] has given us for the development of the great experiment of liberty and federated self-government entrusted to us.

**20.** Which of the following statements best summarizes the views of the writers above?

   **A** Each writer claims that lands in North America have been granted to a certain group of people by a divine power.
   **B** Each writer argues for the right of Native Americans to remain on the lands where they currently lived.
   **C** Each writer supports the right of the United States government to expand its authority across the North America continent.
   **D** Each writer believes Native Americans and the United States government will compromise over land ownership issues.

Name _____ Date _____ Class _____

## TEST B — CRITICAL THINKING AND READING

**Directions:** *Read the passage below. Then answer questions 1–4.*

At the Battle of Gettysburg in July 1863, both the North and the South suffered heavy casualties. On November 19, 1863, President Abraham Lincoln visited Gettysburg to dedicate the battlefield cemetery, and delivered the following speech.

---

### The Gettysburg Address

Four score and seven years ago our fathers brought forth on this continent, a new nation, conceived in liberty, and dedicated to the proposition that all men are created equal.

Now we are engaged in a great civil war, testing whether that nation, or any nation so conceived and so dedicated, can long endure. We are met on a great battlefield of that war. We have come to dedicate a portion of that field, as a final resting place for those who here gave their lives that that nation might live. It is altogether fitting and proper that we should do this. But in a larger sense, we cannot dedicate—we cannot consecrate—we cannot hallow—this ground. The brave men, living and dead, who struggled here have consecrated it, far above our poor power to add or detract. The world will little note, nor long remember what we say here, but it can never forget what they did here. It is for us the living, rather, to be dedicated here to the unfinished work which they who fought here have thus far so nobly advanced. It is rather for us to be here dedicated to the great task remaining before us—that from these honored dead we take increased devotion to that cause for which they gave the last full measure of devotion—that we here highly resolve that these dead shall not have died in vain—that this nation, under God, shall have a new birth of freedom—and that government of the people, by the people, for the people shall not perish from the earth.

---

1. What does President Lincoln say is the *best* way to honor the soldiers who have died at the Battle of Gettysburg?

    A Attack the enemy forces on the great battlefield of Gettysburg.

    B Keep the principles of democracy that they died for alive.

    C Seek immediate revenge on those who would threaten democracy.

    D Refuse to be drawn into another meaningless war.

2. What is the "unfinished work" that President Lincoln believes the American people still have to do?

    A They need to ensure that the principles of our nation do not fail.

    B They need to consecrate the soldiers who have fought in all wars.

    C They need to continue to expand America's borders.

    D They need to ensure that foreign nations do not destroy the Union.

3. What is the *most likely* effect of President Lincoln's speech?

    A Listeners will be discouraged from supporting the war effort.

    B The government of the United States will be dissolved.

    C Congress will withdraw support for a memorial at Gettysburg.

    D Listeners will have greater dedication to Lincoln's cause.

4. What might have been one reason that President Lincoln chose to give a speech about the future of the nation when dedicating the Gettysburg cemetery?

    A to consecrate the ground in memory of the dead soldiers

    B to emphasize that no one died in vain, and that we must continue their fight

    C to encourage young men to fight for freedom by enlisting

    D to cause families to fear that their sons might perish in the war

GO ON

## T E S T  B — CRITICAL THINKING AND READING *(continued)*

**Directions:** *Read the story* "The Envious Buffalo" *from* The Fables of India, *retold by Joseph Gaer. Then answer questions 5–8.*

On a small farm in southern India there lived a water buffalo named Big Red Bubalus with his younger brother named Little Red Bubalus. These two brothers did all the hard work on the farm. They plowed and they harrowed; they seeded; and they brought in the harvest for their owner.

Yet for all their labors they were rarely rewarded. And all they were given to eat was grass and straw, or chaff when the grain was husked.

This same farmer owned a pig who did nothing but eat and wallow in the water pumped up for him by the buffaloes. Yet the hog was fed on rice and millet and was well taken care of by the farmer and his family.

Little Red Bubalus complained to his brother: "We, who do all the hard work, are treated shabbily and our master gives us next to nothing to eat. Most of the time we have to go out into the pasture to find our own food. Yet this lazy pig is fed all the time and never does any work."

"Envy him not, little brother," said Big Red Bubalus. . . .

One day the farmer's only daughter was engaged to be married. And as the wedding day drew near, the hog was slaughtered and roasted for the wedding feast.

Then Big Red Bubalus said to Little Red Bubalus: "Now do you see why a pig is not to be envied?"

And Little Red Bubalus replied: "Yes, now I understand. It is better to feed on straw and chaff, and to live out our lives, than to be fattened on rice only to end up on a roasting spit."

**5.** This story is a fable that teaches a lesson about life called a *moral*. What is the moral of this story?

   **A** Do not waste time working when you can rest.
   **B** Do not wish for what you can never have.
   **C** We should not envy others but should appreciate the good in our own lives.
   **D** Only buffaloes have to suffer.

**6.** What happens after Little Red Bubalus complains?

   **A** Big Red Bubalus says nothing.
   **B** Big Red Bubalus responds, "Envy him not, little brother."
   **C** The pig is rewarded with rice and millet.
   **D** Big Red Bubalus is punished.

**7.** the pig : _____ :: the buffaloes : _____

   **A** business people, rich people
   **B** young people, old people
   **C** leisurely people, hard-working people
   **D** messy people, neat people

**8.** How does understanding the situation help Little Red Bubalus?

   **A** It helps Little Red Bubalus understand that someday he will be like the pig.
   **B** It helps Little Red Bubalus understand that Big Red Bubalus is wrong.
   **C** It helps Little Red Bubalus understand that his work has reward.
   **D** It helps Little Red Bubalus understand that now he will be fed millet.

GO ON

## TEST B — CRITICAL THINKING AND READING *(continued)*

**Directions:** *Read the passage below that describes the Korean martial art of* tae kwon do. *Then answer questions 9–12.*

The martial arts are ways of fighting . . . but a person who [practices the martial arts] tries to act in ways that bring peace. [Those who practice the martial arts] do not fight in real life unless there is no other choice. Koreans developed the martial art of *tae kwon do* more than 2,000 years ago. Today, it is one of the most popular martial arts in the world.

The name tae kwon do means "the art of kicking and punching." Tae kwon do is especially famous for its jumping and spinning kicks. Before they can do a kick, however, students must block or move out of the way of kicks and punches that are coming toward them. Students of tae kwon do combine quick, straight movements with circular, flowing movements.

To students of tae kwon do, their art is more than a way to defend themselves. It is a way of life. Students learn the following rules:

• be loyal to your country, your school, and your friends
• respect your family, your teachers, and your elders
• maintain a strong spirit and never give up
• finish what you begin

Tae kwon do students promise to follow these rules. They also vow to work hard and keep up with schoolwork. But most of all, they commit themselves to behaving in ways that are kind and peaceful.

**9.** Which of the following statements *best* characterizes tae kwon do?

**A** It is a martial art that teaches you how to defend yourself without having to work out solutions with your enemy.

**B** It is a martial art that allows people to learn new ways to harm their enemies.

**C** It is a martial art that teaches students how to defend themselves and how to live their lives in a peaceful way.

**D** It is a martial art that involves commitment and sacrifice without loyalty to any one nation or ruler.

**10.** Which of the following people is following the lessons taught in tae kwon do?

**A** Despite getting low grades on his spelling test last week, Juan studied even harder for his test the following week.

**B** Marguerite told her older brother that her middle school was the worst in the city.

**C** Aaron practiced his kicks all evening, even though he promised his mother he would spend the evening studying.

**D** Instead of finishing her homework, Rachel went to the pep rally to root for her friends on the football team.

**11.** If someone thought that tae kwon do involved jumping in a fighting ring and kicking your opponent as many times as possible, in what way would they be wrong?

**A** Tae kwon do is a way to defend oneself, but it is more than that because it is also a way of life.

**B** Tae kwon do students must spend most of their time studying and thinking.

**C** Tae kwon do is a way of life, and those who practice it today never use it for fighting.

**D** Tae kwon do is not fought in a ring anymore, but fighters still do this if it is necessary.

**12.** How might tae kwon do help provide the discipline necessary for one to lead a successful life?

**A** Tae kwon do teaches students that physical strength is important.

**B** Tae kwon do improves one's intelligence.

**C** Tae kwon do forbids students from fighting.

**D** Tae kwon do teaches students not to give up and always to do their best.

Name _____ Date _____ Class _____

**T E S T  B — CRITICAL THINKING AND READING** *(continued)*

***Directions:*** *The passage below is from Jennifer Seymour Whitaker's book,* How Can Africa Survive? *It describes the changes that European colonization brought to the traditional role of women in Africa. Read the passage below. Then answer questions 13–16.*

[T]he small farmers who represent most of Africa's populace are politically mute. And none more so than Africa's women farmers, who grow perhaps 70 percent of the continent's food. . . .

In the pre-colonial era, both worked within the subsistence economy. Women farmed and did household chores, while men focused on hunting and war and helped with clearing land and harvesting . . . An African woman often lived a life quite separately economically from that of her husband, in which the basic unit was herself and her children. . . . Her husband most often provided her with a hut and some land

to farm. She sustained her family by working the land allotted to her and by trading . . .

[H]owever, with the introduction of cash crops by the colonial administrators, the division of labor shifted further against women. . . . Regarding wives as homemakers and husbands as breadwinners, the Europeans either did not understand or refused to accept the fact that most African farming was done by women. . . .

Twenty-five years of independence have done little to redress this balance. Because women are even poorer than their husbands and brothers, they are correspondingly less able to make the investments necessary to maintain or increase [crop] yields. . . .

**13.** Which of the following statements *best* expresses Whitaker's viewpoint?

A The division of labor in Africa has caused many wars.

B The division of labor in Africa changes with the seasons.

C The division of labor has hurt women in Africa.

D Labor has always been divided equally between men and women in Africa.

**14.** How was the division of labor in pre-colonial Africa different than that of present-day Africa?

A The division of labor was more equal in pre-colonial Africa, but it changed with the introduction of cash crops.

B The division of labor was different in pre-colonial Africa because men did all the household chores.

C The division of labor was different in pre-colonial Africa because women focused on hunting and war.

D The division of labor was different in pre-colonial Africa because women were regarded as breadwinners.

**15.** According to the passage, which of the following solutions would Whitaker *most likely* support to improve the condition of women farmers in Africa?

A education and training to help women farmers learn farming techniques

B an increase in taxes on imported food and farming equipment

C loans to help women farmers buy better farming equipment, seed, and other necessary items

D stricter marriage and divorce laws to prevent the breakup of families

**16.** With which statement would Whitaker *most likely* disagree?

A European colonialists introduced export crops that hurt the welfare of the continent of Africa as a whole.

B European colonialists accepted the fact that most of the farming in Africa was done by women.

C European colonialists helped create a situation in which women farmers in Africa can barely survive.

D European colonialists set a standard in Africa that is harmful to women today.

# TEST A — COMMUNICATIONS

**Directions:** *Read the following statements about Adolf Hitler, dictator of Germany from 1933 to 1945. Then answer questions 1–4.*

1. Adolf Hitler was born in Branau, Austria, in 1889.
2. While in jail after an unsuccessful attempt to overthrow the Bavarian government, Hitler wrote *Mein Kampf*.
3. *Mein Kampf* is one of the most influential political books ever written.
4. Hitler gave himself the title *Führer* ("Leader") in 1934.
5. Two of Hitler's foreign policy goals were the destruction of the Treaty of Versailles and the transformation of Germany into a military power in Europe.
6. If Hitler had not been so egotistical, he would have succeeded in his plans to dominate Europe.
7. Hitler was stubborn; he refused to leave his headquarters in Berlin, Germany, when the Soviets arrived in the city.
8. Hitler, the most brutal dictator the world has ever known, was responsible for the mass extermination of nearly six million Jews.

1. If you were giving a speech arguing that Hitler had several objectives after gaining power, which of the following statements should you use as evidence?

   A Statement 6    C Statement 4
   B Statement 5    D Statement 8

2. Jacob has concluded that Hitler was a cruel leader. Which statement *best* supports Jacob's conclusion?

   A Statement 5    C Statement 7
   B Statement 6    D Statement 8

3. Which of the following people would be the *most* reliable source for Statement 7?

   A a French soldier who fought in the war
   B an German officer who was with Hitler that day
   C an American reporter based in France
   D an American citizen who worked in weapons factories during the war

4. Maria is writing a paragraph in her history class about the book *Mein Kampf*. Statement 2 is her first sentence. Statement 3 is her second sentence, and it states the main idea of her paragraph. Which of the following statements would be the *most* effective third sentence?

   A The title means "My Struggle," and the work is particularly interesting because it became the guidebook of Hitler's government.
   B Hitler was hated by many people who feared his rapid rise to power.
   C The book is boring because it discusses issues that affected Germany and Poland but not the United States.
   D Had he left his headquarters in Berlin when the Soviets arrived, Hitler would have dominated most of Europe.

GO ON

**TEST A — COMMUNICATIONS** *(continued)*

***Directions:*** *Read the passage below. Compare the passage with the information on the time line. Then answer questions 5–8.*

> Some emperors made strong efforts to stop the steady decline of the Roman Empire. Although Diocletian persecuted Christians, he also worked to strengthen Rome. He enlarged the army and built new forts at the borders. He also improved the system of collecting taxes. This brought in more money to pay the army. Diocletian divided the empire into two parts to make it easier to rule. He ruled over the more wealthy east and appointed a co-emperor to rule over the west.

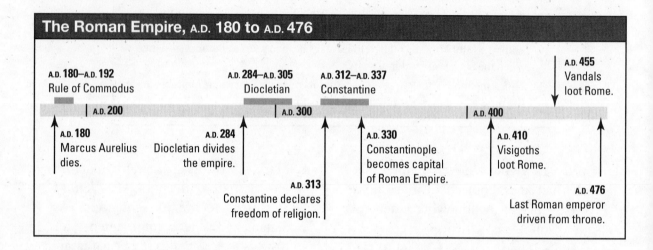

**5.** Which of the events on the time line is the passage *most likely* describing?

  **A** Marcus Aurelius dies.
  **B** Diocletian divides the empire.
  **C** Constantine declares freedom of religion.
  **D** Constantinople becomes capital of the Roman Empire.

**6.** When did the Visigoths loot Rome?

  **A** A.D. 180        **C** A.D. 410
  **B** A.D. 330        **D** A.D. 455

**7.** In A.D. 212, all free people in the Roman Empire were granted citizenship. Where on the time line should this event be placed?

  **A** between A.D. 313 and A.D. 330
  **B** between A.D. 180 and A.D. 284
  **C** between A.D. 410 and A.D. 455
  **D** between A.D. 330 and A.D. 410

**8.** In what year did Diocletian divide the Roman Empire?

  **A** A.D. 180        **C** A.D. 305
  **B** A.D. 284        **D** A.D. 330

**GO ON**

**T E S T   A — COMMUNICATIONS** *(continued)*

*Directions: Read the numbered items below. Then answer questions 9–12.*

---

1. Scientists think that the first people to inhabit North America migrated from Asia some 30,000 years ago.
2. Native Americans eventually populated almost every spot on the continent.
3. After the arrival of Europeans, ways of life for Native Americans began to change.
4. Thousands of Native Americans died from European diseases.
5. Europeans forced Native Americans to move from their lands and work in mines or on farms.

---

**9.** Suppose that you want to write a report arguing that the arrival of Europeans had a negative effect on Native Americans. Which of the statements above would *best* support your position?

A  Statement 1       C  Statement 3
B  Statement 2       D  Statement 4

**10.** Suppose that you had to transfer the events of this passage onto a time line. What is the *best way* to organize the events in Statements 1, 3, 4, and 5?

A  in order of importance
B  according to location
C  in alphabetical order
D  in chronological order

**11.** According to the numbered items, what effect did the arrival of the Europeans have on the Native American population in North America?

A  They relocated to Asia
B  Many died from diseases.
C  They purchased mines and farms.
D  Their lifestyle changed very little.

**12.** If you learned that this passage was written in 1885, what might you reasonably conclude?

A  The information is probably valid because by 1885 all historical information from this earlier period would have been checked.
B  The information is probably valid because it was written by an unbiased source who was an expert in early North America.
C  The information may be flawed because it is old, and scientists may have made many discoveries about early history since 1885.
D  The information may be flawed because it presents only facts that are negative about the arrival of Europeans.

**T E S T   A — COMMUNICATIONS** *(continued)*

*Directions:  Read the two passages below. Then answer questions 13–16.*

**Passage 1:**  Canada is a very diverse country. Its diversity can be seen at one radio station in the city of Toronto, which broadcasts in 30 languages. One of the largest ethnic groups is the French Canadians of Quebec. Many French Canadians want to break away from Canada to form their own country. They have struggled to have the Canadian government recognize and respect their heritage and language. Their work has resulted in Canada's being a bilingual country, in which both English and French are official languages.

**Passage 2:**  Most immigrants to the United States hold on to some of their old customs. In this way, they can keep a sense of identity in their new land. At the same time, they have helped enrich American culture. Artists, writers, and musicians all add to this mix by combining aspects of American culture with elements from other cultures around the world.

**13.** Which statement *best* summarizes the information presented in both passages?

**A** Canada and the United States are countries with large populations made up of a single ethnic group.

**B** Canada and the United States are countries made up of diverse populations with strong cultural identities.

**C** Canada and the United States have immigrant populations that break away from old customs and cultural ties.

**D** Canada and the United States are small countries with populations that speak only a few languages.

**14.** According to the passages, how might your life be different if you were Canadian rather than American?

**A** If you were a Canadian, you would not have to struggle to find acceptance for your cultural identity.

**B** If you were a Canadian, you would lack a cultural identity that most people in the United States enjoy.

**C** If you were a Canadian, you might be taught both French and English, which are both official languages in Canada.

**D** If you were a Canadian, you might have to listen only to French-language radio stations.

**15.** Suppose that you are giving a speech that describes Canada as a very diverse land. Which statement would *most* effectively support your position?

**A** The population of Canada is scattered across a wide area.

**B** A radio station in Toronto broadcasts in 30 languages.

**C** The largest ethnic group in Canada is French Canadians.

**D** French is widely spoken in the Canadian province of Quebec.

**16.** According to the information in both passages, why do *most* immigrants to Canada and the United States preserve many of their original customs?

**A** They never believed they would settle permanently in America or Canada.

**B** They hope to return someday to their native lands.

**C** They want to maintain their cultural identity in their new countries.

**D** They do not like the customs of their adopted countries.

Name _____ Date _____ Class _____

# TEST A — COMMUNICATIONS *(continued)*

*Directions: Examine the chart below. Then answer questions 17–20.*

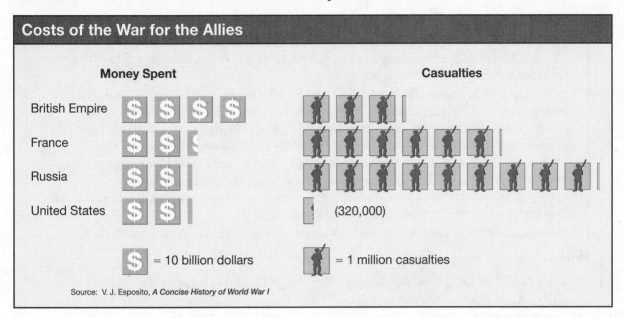

Costs of the War for the Allies

**Money Spent**

British Empire $ $ $ $

France $ $ $

Russia $ $ |

United States $ $ |

**Casualties**

British Empire

France

Russia

United States (320,000)

$ = 10 billion dollars

= 1 million casualties

Source: V. J. Esposito, *A Concise History of World War I*

17. Which of the following statements *best* characterizes the information on the chart about World War I expenses and casualties?

  **A** The United States spent the least on the war and had the fewest casualties.
  **B** Although Russia spent less than the British and French did on the war, it had the most casualties.
  **C** The British Empire spent the most on the war and had the most casualties.
  **D** The war cost each country approximately 1 million casualties for every 10 billion dollars it spent.

18. Which country spent over $20 billion and had over 7 million casualties?

  **A** the British Empire
  **B** France
  **C** Russia
  **D** the United States

19. How much money did the British Empire spend on the World War I effort?

  **A** $4 billion     **C** $40 billion
  **B** $2 billion     **D** $20 billion

20. According to the chart, which two countries spent about the same amount of money?

  **A** France and Russia
  **B** the British Empire and France
  **C** the British Empire and the United States
  **D** Russia and the United States

## T E S T   B — COMMUNICATIONS

*Directions: Read the following passage. Then answer questions 1–3.*

> As in America, Japanese elementary and secondary schools run from first to twelfth grade. But as far as similarities go, that is about it.
>
> To begin with, Japan's school year runs two months longer than America's. Japanese students go to school Monday through Friday, with a half day on Saturday. Altogether, they attend school 240 days out of the year, compared with the American average of 180. The Japanese have one spring vacation and one summer vacation, each three weeks long. . . .
>
> After school, 80 percent of the students attend *juku*, or "cram school," for extra study, or they have private tutors. They do this to prepare for Japan's rigorous system of entrance exams. Students are free to attend any school they wish as long as they pass its admittance test. The best schools have the most demanding exams. . . .
>
> Few American students would find the Japanese system desirable. But it produces results.

1. Which of the following statements *best* supports the conclusion of this passage?

   **A** Japanese students study history, economics, and literature during their high school years.

   **B** Ten percent of all Chinese students attend college at Japanese universities, which are highly regarded.

   **C** According to a study by Stanford University, more United States students are attending colleges today than in the past.

   **D** An estimated 94 percent of Japanese students graduate from high school, compared with less than 80 percent of United States students.

2. In a comparison chart based on this passage, which of the following column titles would be followed by the *most* entries?

   **A** Ways Japanese Education Is Different From United States Education

   **B** Ways United States Education Is Similar to Japanese Education

   **C** Ways High School Is Different From Middle School

   **D** Ways the Japanese School Day Is Different From the United States School Day

3. Michiko is an exchange student from Japan. She is in your class, but seems to be several years ahead in her studies than you and your classmates. Which of the following is the *best* conclusion you can make about this observation, based on the information in the passage?

   **A** It may not be accurate because you cannot compare Michiko's studies to those of her American classmates.

   **B** It may be accurate because Michiko has likely spent more time in class and faced stricter requirements than American students her age.

   **C** It may be accurate because Michiko may be several years older, as most Japanese students are.

   **D** It may not be accurate because Michiko may not be ahead of her classmates in her home country.

32

# TEST B — COMMUNICATIONS (continued)

**Directions:** *Read the passage below. Then answer questions 4–7.*

---

**The Great Serpent Mound**

The serpent mound in Ohio served a very different purpose from that of Cahokia's pyramid mounds. The twisting, snakelike structure was a cemetery. Called the Great Serpent Mound, it is just one of many similar mounds in Ohio. When you look at these mounds from above, they are shaped like animals. Some served as graves for as many as 1,000 people.

The mounds also hold some of the precious belongings of the Mound Builders. Researchers probing the serpent mounds have found jewelry made of shell and copper, clay statues, and other works of art. Some of these items are made from materials that are not from Ohio. Therefore, researchers believe that the Mound Builders must have been involved in extensive trading.

---

4. You are an archaeologist digging at a site in Illinois. You uncover a beautiful clay pot. After some study, you determine that the paint material used to decorate the pot is not from the Illinois area. Using the same reasoning that is presented in the passage, what would you *most likely* conclude?

   **A** The pot is part of a mass grave system in the shape of an animal.
   **B** The pot is not part of the Great Serpent Mound.
   **C** The pot was painted with materials received by trade.
   **D** The pot is from Cahokia's pyramid mounds.

5. For what purpose was the Great Serpent Mound built?

   **A** It was used as a temple.
   **B** It was used for flood prevention.
   **C** It was used as a burial ground.
   **D** It was used in religious ceremonies.

6. Jennifer's class studied the Mound Builders, and now she wants to go to Ohio to see the Great Serpent Mound for herself. In an effort to persuade her mother to take her there for a weekend vacation, she pleads, "Mom, please, we have to go! The Great Serpent Mound is the only one ever built." Jennifer's mother could dispute this argument using what piece of information from the passage?

   **A** The Great Serpent Mound is no longer in Ohio, but is now in Wisconsin.
   **B** The Great Serpent Mound is just one of many similar mounds in Ohio.
   **C** The Great Serpent Mound is very similar to Cahokia's pyramid mounds.
   **D** The Great Serpent Mound takes much longer than a weekend to locate.

7. According to the passage, which of the following is a true statement about the Mound Builders?

   **A** They did not bury their dead.
   **B** A complex system of canals was used to move dirt.
   **C** They were known for burying their enemies alive.
   **D** They lived in what is now the central part of the United States.

# TEST B — COMMUNICATIONS *(continued)*

**Directions:** *Study the following table. Then answer questions 8–10.*

| Rival Plans for Reconstruction | | | | |
|---|---|---|---|---|
| **Plan** | **Ten Percent Plan** | **Wade-Davis Bill** | **Johnson Plan** | **Reconstruction Act** |
| **Proposed by** | President Abraham Lincoln (1863) | Republicans in Congress (1864) | President Andrew Johnson (1865) | Radical Republicans (1867) |
| **Conditions for former Confederate states to rejoin Union** | ▪ 10 percent of voters must swear loyalty to Union<br>▪ Must abolish slavery | ▪ Majority of white men must swear loyalty<br>▪ Former Confederate volunteers cannot vote or hold office | ▪ Majority of white men must swear loyalty<br>▪ Must ratify Thirteenth Amendment<br>▪ Former Confederate officials may vote and hold office | ▪ Must disband state governments<br>▪ Must write new constitutions<br>▪ Must ratify Fourteenth Amendment<br>▪ African American men must be allowed to vote |

**8.** Which of the plans listed in the table would have punished the Confederate states *most* severely?

A Ten Percent Plan
B Wade-Davis Bill
C Johnson Plan
D Reconstruction Act

**9.** If you discovered that this table had been compiled by a former Confederate soldier, what might you suspect about it?

A The information is not current because it is over a hundred years old and the soldier is dead.
B The information is probably not biased because the soldier has no personal interest in which option is chosen.
C The information may be biased because the soldier will be affected directly by the conditions.
D The information lacks authority because a soldier is unable to compile facts.

**10.** You are politically active during the Reconstruction era, and you are making a speech to a group of citizens. In your speech, you argue that slavery must be abolished in the United States, that southern white men must swear loyalty to the Union, and that state governments should be excused from rewriting new constitutions. You also say that African Americans should not be allowed to vote, but that former Confederate officials can. Which of the following plans would you *most likely* support?

A Ten Percent Plan
B Johnson Plan
C Wade-Davis Bill
D Reconstruction Act

## T E S T  B — COMMUNICATIONS (continued)

**Directions:** Look at the table below. Then answer questions 11–16.

### World War II Deaths

|  | Military Dead | Civilian Dead |
|---|---|---|
| Britain | 389,000 | 65,000 |
| France | 211,000 | 108,000 |
| Soviet Union | 7,500,000 | 15,000,000 |
| United States | 292,000 | * |
| Germany | 2,850,000 | 5,000,000 |
| Italy | 77,500 | 100,000 |
| Japan | 1,576,000 | 300,000 |

*Very small number
All figures are estimates
Source: Henri Michel, *The Second World War*

**11.** In a report detailing the human losses incurred during the war, Justin wanted to note which country suffered the *most* casualties during World War II. What should his report say about total casualties?

   **A** The United States suffered more casualties than any other nation.
   **B** The Soviet Union suffered more casualties than any other nation.
   **C** Britain suffered more casualties than any other nation.
   **D** France suffered more casualties than any other nation.

**12.** In which country was the difference between the number of military deaths and the number of civilian deaths the *greatest*?

   **A** Germany      **C** Britain
   **B** Japan        **D** the Soviet Union

**13.** The number of U.S. civilian dead was such a small number that it wasn't estimated on this chart. Which of the following countries had the fewest number of civilian dead compared against its military dead?

   **A** Soviet Union   **C** Italy
   **B** Germany        **D** Japan

**14.** Using this table in a report he gave to his history class, Juan said, "Despite having 292,000 military casualties, the United States had very few civilian casualties. Its ally, the Soviet Union, had exactly 7,500,000 military dead and exactly 15,000,000 civilians dead during the war." What is wrong with Juan's statement?

   **A** The figures about the war deaths are incorrect.
   **B** The United States had a significant number of civilian deaths.
   **C** The figures in the table are estimates, so the number of Soviet deaths is not exact.
   **D** The Soviet Union suffered more military deaths than civilian deaths.

**15.** According to the information in the table, which of the following could you *most likely* conclude?

   **A** Given the number of military deaths, many battles were probably fought in the United States.
   **B** Given the relatively low number of casualties, Italian soldiers were probably highly skilled.
   **C** Given the high number of casualties, the Soviet Union probably started the war.
   **D** Given the number of civilian deaths, many battles were probably fought in Germany and the Soviet Union.

**16.** Which of the following countries is estimated to have twice as many military deaths as civilian deaths during World War II?

   **A** Britain          **C** the United States
   **B** France           **D** Japan

**T E S T  B — COMMUNICATIONS** *(continued)*

**Directions:** *Examine the two graphs below. Then answer questions 17–20.*

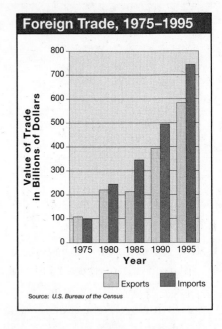

**17.** Compare both graphs about foreign trade in the United States. Which of the following statements about the graphs is true?

   **A** Since 1865, the average value of U.S. foreign trade has remained the same.
   **B** In general, from 1865 to 1915 and from 1975 to 1995, the value of U.S. foreign trade has steadily risen.
   **C** The difference between the amount U.S. exports and the amount it imports has been roughly equal since 1856.
   **D** Between 1975 and 1995, the U.S. generally exported more goods than it imported.

**18.** According to the information in the two graphs, what can you accurately conclude about the period between 1916 and 1974?

   **A** The trend must have changed because that is what trends do.
   **B** The value in billions of dollars continued to increase each year, resulting in an upward, positive trend.
   **C** Nothing; information about this time period is not shown in the graphs.
   **D** The trend was similar, and the trade deficit increased at or near the same rate between time periods.

**19.** A trade surplus exists when a country exports more goods than it imports. In which of the following years did the United States experience a trade surplus?

   **A** 1975        **C** 1990
   **B** 1980        **D** 1995

**20.** You have to write a report about U.S. foreign trade, and you want to include the difference between the goods the United States sells to other countries and the goods it buys from other countries over a single ten-year time period. Which graph would be *best* to include in your report and why?

   **A** The bar graph would be better to use because it includes trade by imports and exports.
   **B** The bar graph would be better to use because its information is more current than the information in the line graph.
   **C** The line graph would be better to use because the results include the value of trade in billions of dollars.
   **D** The line graph would be better to use because it breaks down trade in ten-year periods.

STOP

| Middle Grades Diagnostic Correlations *(continued)* | Test Item(s) | The American Nation, Survey | Civics: Participating in Government | World Explorer: Africa | World Explorer: The Ancient World | World Explorer: Asia and the Pacific |
|---|---|---|---|---|---|---|
| **Communications, Test A** | | | | | | |
| Using Reliable Information | 3, 12 | SE: pp. 556, 795 TE: pp. 671, 793 TR: U6, p. 5 U8, p. 37 | SE: pp. 146, 149, 261, 363 | SE: pp. 58–59 | SE: pp. 24–25, 184–185 | TR: Social Studies and Geography Skills, p. 100 |
| Transferring Information from One Medium to Another | 5, 6, 7, 8, 10, 17, 18, 20 | SE: pp. 297, 899 TE: p. 899 TR: U9, p. 38 | SE: pp. 281, 325, 429 | SE: p. 27 TE: pp. 44, 72, 111, 173 | SE: pp. 24–25 TE: pp. 22, 28C | SE: p. 28 TE: pp. 15, 76–77, 94, 112, 162C |
| Synthesizing Information | 11, 13, 14, 16, 19 | SE: p. 315 TE: pp. 211, 531, 593 TR: U3, p. 21 | SE: pp. 6, 47, 193, 203, 325, 415, 482 | SE: Chapter reviews TE: pp. 30C, 98, 134C, 173 | SE: Chapter reviews TE: pp. 71, 88 | SE: Chapter reviews TE: p. 63 |
| Supporting a Position | 1, 2, 4, 9, 15 | SE: pp. 220, 250, 323, 594, 637, 753 TE: p. 246D | SE: pp. 39, 74, 215, 281, 325, 409 | SE: pp. 46, 61, 103, 114, 155 TE: pp. 24, 78, 113 | SE: pp. 145, 148 | SE: pp. 16, 86, 95 TE: p. 136 |
| **Communications, Test B** | | | | | | |
| Using Reliable Information | 3, 9 | SE: pp. 556, 795 TE: pp. 671, 793 TR: U6, p. 5 U8, p. 37 | SE: pp. 146, 149, 261, 363 | SE: pp. 58–59 | SE: pp. 24–25, 184–185 | TR: Social Studies and Geography Skills, p. 100 |
| Transferring Information from One Medium to Another | 2, 8, 11, 12, 13, 14, 16, 18, 19 | SE: pp. 297, 899 TE: p. 899 TR: U9, p. 38 | SE: pp. 281, 325, 429 | SE: p. 27 TE: pp. 44, 72, 111, 173 | SE: pp. 24–25 TE: pp. 22, 28C | SE: p. 28 TE: pp. 15, 76–77, 94, 112, 162C |
| Synthesizing Information | 5, 7, 15, 17, 18, 20 | SE: p. 315 TE: pp. 211, 531, 593 TR: U3, p. 21 | SE: pp. 6, 47, 193, 203, 325, 415, 482 | SE: Chapter reviews TE: pp. 30C, 98, 134C, 173 | SE: Chapter reviews TE: pp. 71, 88 | SE: Chapter reviews TE: p. 63 |
| Supporting a Position | 1, 4, 6, 10, 20 | SE: pp. 220, 250, 323, 594, 637, 753 TE: p. 246D | SE: pp. 39, 74, 215, 281, 325, 409 | SE: pp. 46, 61, 103, 114, 155 TE: pp. 24, 78, 113 | SE: pp. 145, 148 | SE: pp. 16, 86, 95 TE: p. 136 |
| **Critical Thinking and Reading, Test A** | | | | | | |
| Identifying Main Ideas/ Summarizing | 8, 20 | SE: pp. 61, 116, 124, 130, 341, 444, 553, 562, 756 TR: U1, pp. 21, 54 | SE: Chapter reviews TE: Beginning of each section | SE: Chapter reviews TE: p. 83 TR: pp. 17, 98 | SE: Chapter reviews TR: p. 37; Social Studies and Geography Skills, pp. 41, 42 | SE: Chapter reviews TR: p. 17; Social Studies and Geography Skills, pp. 41, 42 |

SE: Student Edition    TE: Teacher's Edition    TR: Teaching Resources    U: Unit Booklet

| World Explorer: Europe and Russia | World Explorer: Geography: Tools and Concepts | World Explorer: Latin America | World Explorer: Medieval Times to Today | World Explorer: United States and Canada | World Explorer: People, Places, and Cultures, National |
|---|---|---|---|---|---|
| **Communications, Test A** | | | | | |
| SE: pp. 46–47 TR: Social Studies and Geography Skills, p. 100 | SE: pp. 98–99 TR: Social Studies and Geography Skills, p. 100 | SE: pp. 118–119 TR: Social Studies and Geography Skills, p. 100 | SE: pp. 26–27 TR: Social Studies and Geography Skills, p. 100 | SE: pp. 62–63 TR: Social Studies and Geography Skills, p. 100 | SE: pp. 26, 40, 72, 86, 168, 179, 181, 182, 212, 260, 283, 310 TE: p. 359 TR: Social Studies and Geography Skills, p. 100 |
| TE: pp. 8C, 13, 63, 115 | TE: pp. 54C, 104C | TE: pp. 62C, 106C, 109 | SE: pp. 26–27 | SE: pp. 62–63 TE: pp. 86C, 101 | SE: pp. 14, 50, 85, 100, 108, 196, 227, 267, 336, 384 TE: pp. 54C, 104C, 131, 409, 524 |
| SE: Chapter reviews | SE: Chapter reviews TE: p. 85 | SE: Chapter reviews TE: p. 19 | SE: Chapter reviews TE: pp. 98, 173 | SE: Chapter reviews TE: pp. 13, 16, 17, 76, 150–151 | SE: Chapter reviews TE: pp. 49, 156, 375, 433, 453 |
| SE: pp. 45, 53 | SE: pp. 13, 100, 110, 121 | SE: pp. 26, 101 | SE: pp. 110, 142 | TE: p. 77 | SE: pp. 13, 100, 110, 121, 287, 331, 388, 371, 521, 579 TE: p. 191 |
| **Communications, Test B** | | | | | |
| SE: pp. 46–47 TR: Social Studies and Geography Skills, p. 100 | SE: pp. 98–99 TR: Social Studies and Geography Skills, p. 100 | SE: pp. 118–119 TR: Social Studies and Geography Skills, p. 100 | SE: pp. 26–27 TR: Social Studies and Geography Skills, p. 100 | SE: pp. 62–63 TR: Social Studies and Geography Skills, p. 100 | SE: pp. 26, 40, 72, 86, 168, 179, 181, 182, 212, 260, 283, 310 TE: p. 359 TR: Social Studies and Geography Skills, p. 100 |
| TE: pp. 8C, 13, 63, 115 | TE: pp. 54C, 104C | TE: pp. 62C, 106C, 109 | SE: pp. 26–27 | SE: pp. 62–63 TE: pp. 86C, 101 | SE: pp. 14, 50, 85, 100, 108, 196, 227, 267, 336, 384 TE: pp. 54C, 104C, 131, 409, 524 |
| SE: Chapter reviews | SE: Chapter reviews TE: p. 85 | SE: Chapter reviews TE: p. 19 | SE: Chapter reviews TE: pp. 98, 173 | SE: Chapter reviews TE: pp. 13, 16, 17, 76, 150–151 | SE: Chapter reviews TE: pp. 49, 156, 375, 433, 453 |
| SE: pp. 45, 53 | SE: pp. 13, 100, 110, 121 | SE: pp. 26, 101 | SE: pp. 110, 142 | TE: p. 77 | SE: pp. 13, 100, 110, 121, 287, 331, 388, 371, 521, 579 TE: p. 191 |
| **Critical Thinking and Reading, Test A** | | | | | |
| SE: Chapter reviews TE: p. 101 TR: pp. 73, 91 | SE: Chapter reviews TE: p. 83 TR: p. 79 | SE: Chapter reviews TE: p. 123 TR: pp. 52, 67 | SE: pp. 25, 42, Chapter reviews TE: pp. 97, 149, 178 TR: p. 20; Social Studies and Geography Skills, pp. 41, 42 | SE: pp. 28, 45, 64, 67, 137, Chapter reviews TE: pp. 94, 96, 118C, 135, 140 TR: p. 88 | SE: Chapter reviews TE: pp. 127, 174, 231, 309, 395 TR: Social Studies and Geography Skills, pp. 39, 100 |

SE: Student Edition    TE: Teacher's Edition    TR: Teaching Resources    U: Unit Booklet

| Middle Grades Diagnostic Correlations (continued) | Test Item(s) | The American Nation, Survey | Civics: Participating in Government | World Explorer: Africa | World Explorer: The Ancient World | World Explorer: Asia and the Pacific |
|---|---|---|---|---|---|---|
| **Critical Thinking and Reading, Test A (continued)** | | | | | | |
| Sequencing | 5 | SE: pp. 73, 99<br>TE: p. 395<br>TR: U1, p. 37 | SE: p. 42 | TE: p. 30C | SE: pp. 24–25<br>TE: p. 28C | SE: pp. 30–32 |
| Identifying Cause and Effect/Making Predictions | 6, 18 | SE: pp. 120, 161, 291, 314, 345, 442, 706, 815<br>TE: pp. 193, 227, 897<br>TR: U2, p. 5<br>U9, p. 5 | SE: pp. 63, 193, 342, 343, 449, 515<br>TE: pp. 5, 548 | SE: pp. 20, 28, 52, 85, 106, 120<br>TE: pp. 13, 33, 43, 70, 117, 158<br>TR: Social Studies and Geography Skills, p. 50 | SE: pp. 23, 39, 67, 97, 108, 132, 145, 174, 182, 188, 216<br>TE: pp. 23, 48, 99, 157<br>TR: p. 94 | SE: pp. 12, 24, 39, 69, 78, 124, 157<br>TE: p. 42; 165<br>TR: p. 53; Social Studies and Geography Skills, pp. 49, 50, 72 |
| Making Inferences/ Drawing Conclusions | 4, 7, 17 | SE: pp. 95, 104, 211, 256, 295, 436, 547, 643, 663<br>TR: U3, p. 5 | SE: pp. 59, 83, 107, 167, 471<br>TE: p. 17 | SE: pp. 14, 34, 57, 74, 103, 165<br>TE: pp. 153, 164<br>TR: p. 56 | SE: pp. 26, 44, 55, 84, 148, 180, 196<br>TE: pp. 13, 69, 163, 189<br>TR: pp. 16, 58; Social Studies and Geography Skills, p. 52 | SE: pp. 21, 24, 49, 75, 88, 171, 182<br>TE: pp. 18, 52, 121<br>TR: pp. 89, 128; Social Studies and Geography Skills, p. 52 |
| Making Valid Generalizations | 3 | SE: p. 427<br>TR: U4, p. 37 | SE: pp. 54, 235, 409, 423 | SE: Chapter reviews | SE: Chapter reviews | SE: Chapter reviews |
| Distinguishing Fact and Opinion | 10 | SE: pp. 369, 377<br>TR: U4, p. 5 | SE: pp. 212–213, 215 | SE: p. 59<br>TE: p. 101<br>TR: p. 110; Social Studies and Geography Skills, p. 43 | SE: p. 34<br>TE: pp. 109, 126<br>TR: p. 115; Social Studies and Geography Skills, p. 43 | TE: pp. 121, 170<br>TR: p. 110 |
| Comparing and Contrasting | 1, 12 | SE: pp. 90, 115, 347, 353, 428<br>TE: p. 378D<br>TR: U3, p. 38 | SE: pp. 77, 178, 246, 349, 525 | SE: pp. 68, 85, 91, 139<br>TR: pp. 38, 68 | SE: pp. 26, 92, 118, 128, 182<br>TE: p. 6<br>TR: p. 136 | SE: pp. 44, 49, 142, 145, 157, 160<br>TE: p. 132C<br>TR: p. 38 |
| Analyzing Primary and Secondary Sources | 13, 19 | SE: pp. 94, 110, 214, 219, 319, 344, 451, 551, 556, 651, 855<br>TE: pp. 75, 229, 327, 835<br>TR: U2, p. 37<br>U9, p. 22 | SE: pp. 62, 86–87, 95, 108–129, 149, 167, 234, 235, 260, 347<br>TR: Learning with Documents booklet; Citizenship Skills, pp. 6, 22, 58 | SE: pp. 132–133, 156–159<br>TR: Primary Sources and Literature Readings booklet | SE: pp. 120–121, 186–189 | SE: pp. 58–59, 110–113<br>TR: Primary Sources and Literature Readings booklet |
| Recognizing Bias and Propaganda | 2, 11 | SE: pp. 367, 471, 477, 670, 697, 711<br>TE: p. 447<br>TR: U5, p. 5<br>U6, p. 37 | SE: pp. 84, 146, 234, 363 | SE: p. 58<br>TE: p. 59<br>TR: p. 83 | SE: p. 139<br>TE: p. 175 | SE: p. 118<br>TE: p. 39 |

SE: Student Edition  TE: Teacher's Edition  TR: Teaching Resources  U: Unit Booklet

| World Explorer: Europe and Russia | World Explorer: Geography: Tools and Concepts | World Explorer: Latin America | World Explorer: Medieval Times to Today | World Explorer: United States and Canada | World Explorer: People, Places, and Cultures, National |
|---|---|---|---|---|---|
| **Critical Thinking and Reading, Test A** (*continued*) | | | | | |
| TE: p. 32C<br>TR: Social Studies and Geography Skills, p. 61 | SE: pp. 84, 86 | SE: pp. 48–49<br>TE: p. 34C | TE: pp. 10, 17, 91 | SE: p. 151<br>TE: pp. 32C, 35, 39, 133, 140 | SE: pp. 101, 153, 224, 274, 286, 370, 381, 422, 467, 568<br>TE: p. 215 |
| SE: pp. 21, 42, 65, 120, 145, 151, 152, 160, 167<br>TE: pp. 11, 52, 61, 76, 116, 144<br>TR: Social Studies and Geography Skills, pp. 49, 50 | SE: pp. 10, 22, 32, 42, 50, 68, 81, 94, 124<br>TE: pp. 39, 48, 81<br>TR: p. 46 | SE: pp. 27, 56, 59, 67, 77, 86, 93, 116, 154<br>TE: pp. 45, 67, 144 | SE: pp. 13, 15, 20, 33, 40, 76<br>TE: pp. 16, 19, 29, 77<br>TR: p. 134; Social Studies and Geography Skills, pp. 49, 50 | SE: pp. 28, 37, 40, 49, 98<br>TE: pp. 10, 35<br>TR: pp. 16, 67 | SE: pp. 10, 22, 32, 42, 50, 68, 81, 94, 124, 407, 479, 535<br>TE: pp. 28, 39, 48, 88, 201, 413, 556<br>TR: Social Studies and Geography Skills, pp. 47, 48 |
| SE: pp. 15, 29, 49, 103, 126<br>TE: pp. 34, 50, 57, 71, 89, 162<br>TR: p. 16; Social Studies and Geography Skills, p. 52 | SE: pp. 30, 47, 63, 92<br>TE: pp. 11, 33, 41, 67, 112<br>TR: p. 13; Social Studies and Geography Skills, p. 52 | SE: pp. 19, 28, 42, 103, 112, 126, 153<br>TE: pp. 17, 33<br>TR: pp. 16, 37 | SE: pp. 9, 12, 14, 15, 24<br>TE: pp. 9, 191, 205<br>TR: pp. 50, 101; Social Studies and Geography Skills, p. 52 | SE: pp. 11, 13, 14, 17, 19<br>TE: pp. 23, 36, 77<br>TR: p. 37; Social Studies and Geography Skills, p. 52 | SE: pp. 30, 47, 63, 92, 103, 119, 139, 181, 289, 305, 341, 435, 437, 479, 508, 537, 568<br>TE: pp. 11, 33, 41, 45, 112, 115, 300, 425<br>TR: Social Studies and Geography Skills, p. 50 |
| SE: Chapter reviews | SE: Chapter reviews | SE: Chapter reviews | SE: Chapter reviews | SE: Chapter reviews | SE: Chapter reviews<br>TE: p. 167 |
| TE: p. 85<br>TR: p. 52 | SE: pp. 36, 97<br>TE: p. 119<br>TR: p. 31 | SE: pp. 38, 71, 78–79<br>TR: p. 82 | SE: pp. 155, 162–163<br>TE: pp. 18, 162–163<br>TR: p. 65; Social Studies and Geography Skills, p. 43 | TE: pp. 19, 107 | SE: pp. 36, 97, 175, 185, 195, 207, 211, 240, 273, 283, 287, 367, 561<br>TE: pp. 135, 297, 406<br>TR: Social Studies and Geography Skills, p. 41 |
| SE: pp. 8, 39, 79, 116<br>TE: p. 96C<br>TR: p. 37 | SE: p. 69<br>TR: p. 64 | SE: pp. 13, 58, 60, 72, 117, 126, 154<br>TE: p. 106C | SE: pp. 21, 34, 53, 56, 193<br>TE: pp. 22, 108<br>TR: p. 83 | SE: pp. 20, 25, 55, 64, 112<br>TE: pp. 3, 10, 100, 118C, 144<br>TR: p. 49 | SE: pp. 69, 103, 139, 181, 207, 325, 367, 393, 517, 561<br>TE: p. 157 |
| SE: pp. 62, 68–71, 172–173<br>TR: Primary Sources and Literature Readings booklet | SE: pp. 74–75, 102–103<br>TR: Primary Sources and Literature Readings booklet | SE: pp. 30–33, 158–159 | SE: pp. 80–81, 132–135<br>TE: pp. 80, 132, 135<br>TR: Primary Sources and Literature Readings booklet | SE: pp. 84–85, 114–117<br>TE: pp. 84–85, 102, 114–116 | SE: pp. 74–75, 102–103, 117, 139, 273, 289, 376, 418, 517<br>TE: p. 65<br>TR: Primary Sources and Literature Readings booklet |
| SE: pp. 90, 111<br>TE: p. 149 | SE: p. 86<br>TE: p. 89 | SE: pp. 47, 139<br>TE: p. 47 | TE: pp. 177, 213<br>TR: p. 35 | TE: p. 125 | SE: pp. 86, 128M, 155M, 188, 195, 227, 240, 273, 283, 287, 515<br>TE: pp. 53, 89, 143, 187, 332, 485<br>TR: Social Studies and Geography Skills, p. 45 |

SE: Student Edition    TE: Teacher's Edition    TR: Teaching Resources    U: Unit Booklet

| Middle Grades Diagnostic Correlations (continued) | Test Item(s) | The American Nation, Survey | Civics: Participating in Government | World Explorer: Africa | World Explorer: The Ancient World | World Explorer: Asia and the Pacific |
|---|---|---|---|---|---|---|
| **Critical Thinking and Reading, Test A (continued)** | | | | | | |
| Identifying Frame of Reference and Point of View | 9, 14, 20 | SE: pp. 172, 318, 367, 424, 465, 474, 559, 669 TE: pp. 75, 179, 281, 323, 343, 471, 671, 863 TR: U2, p. 20 | SE: p. 234 TE: pp. 32, 162, 244, 353, 569 TR: Simulations and Debates folder; Citizenship Skills, p. 6 | SE: p. 58 | SE: p. 139 | SE: p. 105, 152 |
| Decision Making | 16 | SE: pp. 105, 310, 443, 453 TE: p. 549 TR: U4, p. 53 | SE: pp. 20, 40, 60, 146, 190, 212, 258, 302, 382, 404, 490, 536 TR: Decision-Making Activities folder; Citizenship Skills, pp. 54, 61 | TE: p. 108C | TE: p. 60C | TE: p. 145 |
| Problem Solving | 15, 16 | SE: pp. 520, 535 TR: U5, p. 39 | SE: p. 515 TR: Citizenship Skills, p. 48 | SE: pp. 90–91 TE: pp. 51, 165 | TE: pp. 143, 215 TR: p. 76 | SE: pp. 6, 127 TE: pp. 126, 136, 147 TR: p. 74 |
| **Critical Thinking and Reading, Test B** | | | | | | |
| Identifying Main Ideas/ Summarizing | 9 | SE: pp. 61, 116, 124, 130, 341, 444, 553, 562, 756 TR: U1, pp. 21, 54 | SE: Chapter reviews TE: Beginning of each section | SE: Chapter reviews TE: p. 83 TR: pp. 17, 98 | SE: Chapter reviews TR: p. 37; Social Studies and Geography Skills, pp. 41, 42 | SE: Chapter reviews TR: p. 17; Social Studies and Geography Skills, pp. 41, 42 |
| Sequencing | 6 | SE: pp. 73, 99 TE: p. 395 TR: U1, p. 37 | SE: p. 42 | TE: p. 30C | SE: pp. 24–25 TE: p. 28C | SE: pp. 30–32 |
| Identifying Cause and Effect/Making Predictions | 3 | SE: pp. 120, 161, 291, 314, 345, 442, 706, 815 TE: pp. 193, 227, 897 TR: U2, p. 5 U9, p. 5 | SE: pp. 63, 193, 342, 343, 449, 515 TE: pp. 5, 548 | SE: pp. 20, 28, 52, 85, 106, 120 TE: pp. 13, 33, 43, 70, 117, 158 TR: Social Studies and Geography Skills, p. 50 | SE: pp. 23, 39, 67, 97, 108, 132, 145, 174, 182, 188, 216 TE: pp. 23, 48, 99, 157 TR: p. 94 | SE: pp. 12, 24, 39, 69, 78, 124, 157 TE: pp. 42, 165 TR: p. 53; Social Studies and Geography Skills, pp. 49, 50, 72 |
| Making Inferences/ Drawing Conclusions | 1, 5, 8, 10, 11 | SE: pp. 95, 104, 211, 256, 295, 436, 547, 643, 663 TR: U3, p. 5 | SE: pp. 59, 83, 107, 167, 471 TE: p. 17 | SE: pp. 14, 34, 57, 74, 103, 165 TE: pp. 153, 164 TR: p. 56 | SE: pp. 26, 44, 55, 84, 148, 180, 196 TE: pp. 13, 69, 163, 189 TR: pp. 16, 58; Social Studies and Geography Skills, p. 52 | SE: pp. 21, 24, 49, 75, 88, 171, 182 TE: pp. 18, 52, 121 TR: pp. 89, 128; Social Studies and Geography Skills, p. 52 |
| Making Valid Generalizations | 12 | SE: p. 427 TR: U4, p. 37 | SE: pp. 54, 235, 409, 423 | SE: Chapter reviews | SE: Chapter reviews | SE: Chapter reviews |

SE: Student Edition    TE: Teacher's Edition    TR: Teaching Resources    U: Unit Booklet

| World Explorer: Europe and Russia | World Explorer: Geography: Tools and Concepts | World Explorer: Latin America | World Explorer: Medieval Times to Today | World Explorer: United States and Canada | World Explorer: People, Places, and Cultures, National |
|---|---|---|---|---|---|
| Critical Thinking and Reading, Test A *(continued)* | | | | | |
| SE: pp. 90, 132 | SE: pp. 69, 97 | SE: pp. 67, 101, 117, 125<br>TE: p. 128C | TE: p. 213 | SE: p. 148 | SE: pp. 69, 97, 181, 195, 379, 395, 421, 431, 497, 515, 523, 539, 577<br>TE: p. 317 |
| TE: p. 32C | SE: p. 69 | SE: pp. 13, 147<br>TE: p. 106C | SE: pp. 54–55 | SE: pp. 146–147 | SE: pp. 69, 79, 172, 193, 195, 267, 305, 323, 535, 537<br>TE: p. 313 |
| TE: pp. 50, 145 | SE: pp. 20, 63<br>TR: Social Studies and Geography Skills, p. 40 | SE: pp. 134, 147<br>TE: pp. 101, 128C | SE: pp. 20, 99, 165, 203, 216–217<br>TE: pp. 172, 216–217<br>TR: p. 119; Social Studies and Geography Skills, p. 40 | SE: pp. 43, 61, 82<br>TE: pp. 48, 57, 59, 72 | SE: pp. 63, 193, 267, 323, 343, 383–384, 415–417, 504, 537<br>TE: pp. 222, 328, 429, 471, 533 |
| Critical Thinking and Reading, Test B | | | | | |
| SE: Chapter reviews<br>TE: p. 101<br>TR: pp. 73, 91 | SE: Chapter reviews<br>TE: p. 83<br>TR: p. 79 | SE: Chapter reviews<br>TE: p. 123<br>TR: pp. 52, 67 | SE: pp. 25, 42, Chapter reviews<br>TE: pp. 97, 149, 178<br>TR: p. 20; Social Studies and Geography Skills, pp. 41, 42 | SE: pp. 28, 45, 64, 67, 137, Chapter reviews<br>TE: pp. 94, 96, 118C, 135, 140<br>TR: p. 88 | SE: Chapter reviews<br>TE: pp. 127, 174, 231, 309, 395<br>TR: Social Studies and Geography Skills, pp. 39, 100 |
| TE: p. 32C<br>TR: Social Studies and Geography Skills, p. 61 | SE: pp. 84, 86 | SE: pp. 48–49<br>TE: p. 34C | TE: pp. 10, 17, 91 | SE: p. 151<br>TE: pp. 32C, 35, 39, 133, 140 | SE: pp. 101, 153, 224, 274, 286, 370, 381, 422, 467, 568<br>TE: p. 215 |
| SE: pp. 21, 42, 65, 120, 145, 151, 152, 160, 167<br>TE: pp. 11, 52, 61, 76, 116, 144<br>TR: Social Studies and Geography Skills, pp. 49, 50 | SE: pp. 10, 22, 32, 42, 50, 68, 81, 94, 124<br>TE: pp. 39, 48, 81<br>TR: pp. 46 | SE: pp. 27, 56, 59, 67, 77, 86, 93, 116, 154<br>TE: pp. 45, 67, 144 | SE: pp. 13, 15, 20, 33, 40, 76<br>TE: pp. 16, 19, 29, 77<br>TR: p. 134; Social Studies and Geography Skills, pp. 49, 50 | SE: pp. 28, 37, 40, 49, 98<br>TE: pp. 10, 35<br>TR: pp. 16, 67 | SE: pp. 10, 22, 32, 42, 50, 68, 81, 94, 124, 407, 479, 535<br>TE: pp. 28, 39, 48, 88, 201, 413, 556<br>TR: Social Studies and Geography Skills, pp. 47, 48 |
| SE: pp. 15, 29, 49, 103, 126<br>TE: pp. 34, 50, 57, 71, 89, 162<br>TR: p. 16; Social Studies and Geography Skills, p. 52 | SE: pp. 30, 47, 63, 92<br>TE: pp. 11, 33, 41, 67, 112<br>TR: p. 13; Social Studies and Geography Skills, p. 52 | SE: pp. 19, 28, 42, 103, 112, 126, 153<br>TE: pp. 17, 33<br>TR: pp. 16, 37 | SE: pp. 9, 12, 14, 15, 24<br>TE: pp. 9, 191, 205<br>TR: pp. 50, 101; Social Studies and Geography Skills, p. 52 | SE: pp. 11, 13, 14, 17, 19<br>TE: pp. 23, 36, 77<br>TR: p. 37; Social Studies and Geography Skills, p. 52 | SE: pp. 30, 47, 63, 92, 103, 119, 139, 181, 289, 305, 341, 435, 437, 479, 508, 537, 568<br>TE: pp. 11, 33, 41, 45, 112, 115, 300, 425<br>TR: Social Studies and Geography Skills, p. 50 |
| SE: Chapter reviews | SE: Chapter reviews | SE: Chapter reviews | SE: Chapter reviews | SE: Chapter reviews | SE: Chapter reviews<br>TE: p. 167 |

SE: Student Edition     TE: Teacher's Edition     TR: Teaching Resources     U: Unit Booklet

| Middle Grades Diagnostic Correlations *(continued)* | Test Item(s) | The American Nation, Survey | Civics: Participating in Government | World Explorer: Africa | World Explorer: The Ancient World | World Explorer: Asia and the Pacific |
|---|---|---|---|---|---|---|
| **Critical Thinking and Reading, Test B** *(continued)* | | | | | | |
| Distinguishing Fact and Opinion | 16 | SE: pp. 369, 377<br>TR: U4, p. 5 | SE: pp. 212–213, 215 | SE: p. 59<br>TE: p. 101<br>TR: p. 110; Social Studies and Geography Skills, p. 43 | SE: p. 34<br>TE: pp. 109, 126<br>TR: p. 115; Social Studies and Geography Skills, p. 43 | TE: pp. 121, 170<br>TR: p. 110 |
| Comparing and Contrasting | 7, 14 | SE: pp. 90, 115, 347, 353, 428<br>TE: p. 378D<br>TR: U3, p. 38 | SE: pp. 77, 178, 246, 349, 525 | SE: pp. 68, 85, 91, 139<br>TR: pp. 38, 68 | SE: pp. 26, 92, 118, 128, 182<br>TE: p. 6<br>TR: p. 136 | SE: pp. 44, 49, 142, 145, 157, 160<br>TE: p. 132C<br>TR: p. 38 |
| Analyzing Primary and Secondary Sources | 2, 4 | SE: pp. 94, 110, 214, 219, 319, 344, 451, 551, 556, 651, 855<br>TE: pp. 75, 229, 327, 835<br>TR: U2, p. 37<br>U9, p. 22 | SE: pp. 62, 86–87, 95, 108–129, 149, 167, 234, 235, 260, 347<br>TR: Learning with Documents booklet; Citizenship Skills, pp. 6, 22, 58 | SE: pp. 132–133, 156–159<br>TR: Primary Sources and Literature Readings booklet | SE: pp. 120–121, 186–189 | SE: pp. 58–59, 110–113<br>TR: Primary Sources and Literature Readings booklet |
| Recognizing Bias and Propaganda | 16 | SE: pp. 367, 471, 477, 670, 697, 711<br>TE: p. 447<br>TR: U5, p. 5<br>U6, p. 37 | SE: pp. 84, 146, 234, 363 | SE: p. 58<br>TE: p. 59<br>TR: p. 83 | SE: p. 139<br>TE: p. 175 | SE: p. 118<br>TE: p. 39 |
| Identifying Frame of Reference and Point of View | 13 | SE: pp. 172, 318, 367, 424, 465, 474, 559, 669<br>TE: pp. 75, 179, 281, 323, 343, 471, 671, 863<br>TR: U2, p. 20 | SE: p. 234<br>TE: pp. 32, 162, 244, 353, 569<br>TR: Simulations and Debates folder; Citizenship Skills, p. 6 | SE: p. 58 | SE: p. 139 | SE: pp. 105, 152 |
| Decision Making | 15 | SE: pp. 105, 310, 443, 453<br>TE: p. 549<br>TR: U4, p. 53 | SE: pp. 20, 40, 60, 146, 190, 212, 258, 302, 382, 404, 490, 536<br>TR: Decision-Making Activities folder; Citizenship Skills, pp. 54, 61 | TE: p. 108C | TE: p. 60C | TE: p. 145 |
| Problem Solving | 15 | SE: pp. 520, 535<br>TR: U5, p. 39 | SE: p. 515<br>TR: Citizenship Skills, p. 48 | SE: pp. 90–91<br>TE: pp. 51, 165 | TE: pp. 143, 215<br>TR: p. 76 | SE: pp. 6, 127<br>TE: pp. 126, 136, 147<br>TR: p. 74 |

SE: Student Edition     TE: Teacher's Edition     TR: Teaching Resources     U: Unit Booklet

| World Explorer: Europe and Russia | World Explorer: Geography: Tools and Concepts | World Explorer: Latin America | World Explorer: Medieval Times to Today | World Explorer: United States and Canada | World Explorer: People, Places, and Cultures, National |
|---|---|---|---|---|---|
| **Critical Thinking and Reading, Test B** *(continued)* | | | | | |
| TE: p. 85<br>TR: p. 52 | SE: pp. 36, 97<br>TE: p. 119<br>TR: p. 31 | SE: pp. 38, 71, 78–79<br>TR: p. 82 | SE: pp. 155, 162–163<br>TE: pp. 18, 162–163<br>TR: p. 65; Social Studies and Geography Skills, p. 43 | TE: pp. 19, 107 | SE: pp. 36, 97, 175, 185, 195, 207, 211, 240, 273, 283, 287, 367, 561<br>TE: pp. 135, 297, 406<br>TR: Social Studies and Geography Skills, p. 41 |
| SE: pp. 8, 39, 79, 116<br>TE: p. 96C<br>TR: p. 37 | SE: p. 69<br>TR: p. 64 | SE: pp. 13, 58, 60, 72, 117, 126, 154<br>TE: p. 106C | SE: pp. 21, 34, 53, 56, 193<br>TE: pp. 22, 108<br>TR: p. 83 | SE: pp. 20, 25, 55, 64, 112<br>TE: pp. 3, 10, 100, 118C, 144<br>TR: p. 49 | SE: pp. 69, 103, 139, 181, 207, 325, 367, 393, 517, 561<br>TE: p. 157 |
| SE: pp. 62, 68–71, 172–173<br>TR: Primary Sources and Literature Readings booklet | SE: pp. 74–75, 102–103<br>TR: Primary Sources and Literature Readings booklet | SE: pp. 30–33, 158–159 | SE: pp. 80–81, 132–135<br>TE: pp. 80, 132, 135<br>TR: Primary Sources and Literature Readings booklet | SE: pp. 84–85, 114–117<br>TE: pp. 84–85, 102, 114–116 | SE: pp. 74–75, 102–103, 117, 139, 273, 289, 376, 418, 517<br>TE: p. 65<br>TR: Primary Sources and Literature Readings booklet |
| SE: pp. 90, 111<br>TE: p. 149 | SE: p. 86<br>TE: p. 89 | SE: pp. 47, 139<br>TE: p. 47 | TE: pp. 177, 213<br>TR: p. 35 | TE: p. 125 | SE: pp. 86, 128M, 155M, 188, 195, 227, 240, 273, 283, 287, 515<br>TE: pp. 53, 89, 143, 187, 332, 485<br>TR: Social Studies and Geography Skills, p. 45 |
| SE: pp. 90, 132 | SE: pp. 69, 97 | SE: pp. 67, 101, 117, 125<br>TE: p. 128C | TE: p. 213 | SE: p. 148 | SE: pp. 69, 97, 181, 195, 379, 395, 421, 431, 497, 515, 523, 539, 577<br>TE: p. 317 |
| TE: p. 32C | SE: p. 69 | SE: pp. 13, 147<br>TE: p. 106C | SE: pp. 54–55 | SE: pp. 146–147 | SE: pp. 69, 79, 172, 193, 195, 267, 305, 323, 535, 537<br>TE: p. 313 |
| TE: pp. 50, 145 | SE: pp. 20, 63<br>TR: Social Studies and Geography Skills, p. 40 | SE: pp. 134, 147<br>TE: pp. 101, 128C | SE: pp. 20, 99, 165, 203, 216–217<br>TE: pp. 172, 216–217<br>TR: p. 119; Social Studies and Geography Skills, p. 40 | SE: pp. 43, 61, 82<br>TE: pp. 48, 57, 59, 72 | SE: pp. 63, 193, 267, 384, 504, 323, 343, 383–384, 415–417, 504, 537<br>TE: pp. 222, 328, 429, 471, 533 |

SE: Student Edition    TE: Teacher's Edition    TR: Teaching Resources    U: Unit Booklet

| Middle Grades Diagnostic Correlations (continued) | Test Item(s) | The American Nation, Survey | Civics: Participating in Government | World Explorer: Africa | World Explorer: The Ancient World | World Explorer: Asia and the Pacific |
|---|---|---|---|---|---|---|
| **Geographic Literacy, Test A** | | | | | | |
| Using the Cartographer's Tools | 1, 2, 3, 5, 6, 7, 9, 10, 16 | SE: pp. 10, 142, 201, 308, 340, 390, 469, 507, 611, 664<br>TE: pp. 5, 115, 166D, 379, 432D, 699<br>TR: U1, p. 5<br>U4, p. 20<br>U6, p. 38 | SE: pp. 5, 71, 223, 244, 256, 337, 488, 530, 578, 592, 594 | SE: pp. 104, 116, 126, 141, 146, 162, 169, 183–193<br>TE: pp. 15, 30C, 97<br>TR: Social Studies and Geography Skills, pp. 3, 4, 5, 6, 7, 10, 12, 13, 15, 16, 18, 19, 20, 21, 24, 25, 26, 27, 28, 29, 30, 31, 32, 33, 34, 35, 36, 37, 38, 39 | SE: pp. 90, 229–238<br>TE: pp. 61, 157<br>TR: Social Studies and Geography Skills, pp. 3, 4, 5, 6, 7, 10, 12, 13, 15, 16, 18, 19, 20, 21, 24, 25, 26, 27, 28, 29, 30, 31, 32, 33, 34, 35, 36, 37, 38, 39 | SE: pp. 54, 76, 195–204<br>TE: pp. 15, 97<br>TR: Social Studies and Geography Skills, pp. 3, 4, 5, 6, 7, 10, 12, 13, 15, 16, 18, 19, 20, 21, 24, 25, 26, 27, 28, 29, 30, 31, 32, 33, 34, 35, 36, 37, 38, 39 |
| Analyzing and Interpreting Special Purpose Maps | 4, 8, 11, 12, 13, 14, 15 | SE: pp. 10, 144, 182, 349, 390, 495, 611, 791<br>TE: pp. 5, 115, 301, 329, 459, 599, 699, 773<br>TR: U1, p. 5<br>U4, p. 20<br>U6, p. 38 | SE: pp. 5, 71, 223, 244, 256, 337, 488, 530, 578, 592, 594 | SE: pp. 104, 126, 146, 190–192<br>TE: pp. 15, 97<br>TR: Social Studies and Geography Skills, pp. 3, 4, 5, 6, 7, 10, 12, 13, 15, 16, 18, 19, 20, 21, 24, 25, 26, 27, 28, 29, 30, 31, 32, 33, 34, 35, 36, 37, 38, 39 | SE: pp. 90, 236–238<br>TE: pp. 61, 157<br>TR: Social Studies and Geography Skills, pp. 3, 4, 5, 6, 7, 10, 12, 13, 15, 16, 18, 19, 20, 21, 24, 25, 26, 27, 28, 29, 30, 31, 32, 33, 34, 35, 36, 37, 38, 39 | SE: pp. 54, 76, 202–204<br>TE: pp. 15, 97<br>TR: Social Studies and Geography Skills, pp. 3, 4, 5, 6, 7, 10, 12, 13, 15, 16, 18, 19, 20, 21, 24, 25, 26, 27, 28, 29, 30, 31, 32, 33, 34, 35, 36, 37, 38, 39 |
| **Geographic Literacy, Test B** | | | | | | |
| Using the Cartographer's Tools | 4, 5, 6, 7, 8, 10, 11, 12, 13, 15, 16 | SE: pp. 10, 142, 201, 308, 340, 390, 469, 507, 611, 664<br>TE: pp. 5, 115, 166D, 379, 432D, 699<br>TR: U1, p. 5<br>U4, p. 20<br>U6, p. 38 | SE: pp. 5, 71, 223, 244, 256, 337, 488, 530, 578, 592, 594 | SE: pp. 104, 116, 126, 141, 146, 162, 169, 183–193<br>TE: pp. 15, 30C, 97<br>TR: Social Studies and Geography Skills, pp. 3, 4, 5, 6, 7, 10, 12, 13, 15, 16, 18, 19, 20, 21, 24, 25, 26, 27, 28, 29, 30, 31, 32, 33, 34, 35, 36, 37, 38, 39 | SE: pp. 90, 229–238<br>TE: pp. 61, 157<br>TR: Social Studies and Geography Skills, pp. 3, 4, 5, 6, 7, 10, 12, 13, 15, 16, 18, 19, 20, 21, 24, 25, 26, 27, 28, 29, 30, 31, 32, 33, 34, 35, 36, 37, 38, 39 | SE: pp. 54, 76, 195–204<br>TE: pp. 15, 97<br>TR: Social Studies and Geography Skills, pp. 3, 4, 5, 6, 7, 10, 12, 13, 15, 16, 18, 19, 20, 21, 24, 25, 26, 27, 28, 29, 30, 31, 32, 33, 34, 35, 36, 37, 38, 39 |
| Analyzing and Interpreting Special Purpose Maps | 1, 2, 3, 9, 14, 17 | SE: pp. 10, 144, 182, 349, 390, 495, 611, 791<br>TE: pp. 5, 115, 301, 329, 459, 599, 699, 773<br>TR: U1, p. 5<br>U4, p. 20<br>U6, p. 38 | SE: pp. 5, 71, 223, 244, 256, 337, 488, 530, 578, 592, 594 | SE: pp. 104, 126, 146, 190–192<br>TE: pp. 15, 97<br>TR: Social Studies and Geography Skills, pp. 3, 4, 5, 6, 7, 10, 12, 13, 15, 16, 18, 19, 20, 21, 24, 25, 26, 27, 28, 29, 30, 31, 32, 33, 34, 35, 36, 37, 38, 39 | SE: pp. 90, 236–238<br>TE: pp. 61, 157<br>TR: Social Studies and Geography Skills, pp. 3, 4, 5, 6, 7, 10, 12, 13, 15, 16, 18, 19, 20, 21, 24, 25, 26, 27, 28, 29, 30, 31, 32, 33, 34, 35, 36, 37, 38, 39 | SE: pp. 54, 76, 202–204<br>TE: pp. 15, 97<br>TR: Social Studies and Geography Skills, pp. 3, 4, 5, 6, 7, 10, 12, 13, 15, 16, 18, 19, 20, 21, 24, 25, 26, 27, 28, 29, 30, 31, 32, 33, 34, 35, 36, 37, 38, 39 |

SE: Student Edition    TE: Teacher's Edition    TR: Teaching Resources    U: Unit Booklet

| World Explorer: Europe and Russia | World Explorer: Geography: Tools and Concepts | World Explorer: Latin America | World Explorer: Medieval Times to Today | World Explorer: United States and Canada | World Explorer: People, Places, and Cultures, National |
|---|---|---|---|---|---|
| **Geographic Literacy, Test A** | | | | | |
| SE: pp. 22, 181–190<br>TE: pp. 17, 25, 35, 57<br>TR: Social Studies and Geography Skills, pp. 3, 4, 5, 6, 7, 10, 12, 13, 15, 16, 18, 19, 20, 21, 24, 25, 26, 27, 28, 29, 30, 31, 32, 33, 34, 35, 36, 37, 38, 39 | SE: pp. 2–7, 14–19, 70<br>TE: pp. 41, 57, 113<br>TR: Social Studies and Geography Skills, pp. 3, 7, 10, 11, 25, 26, 31, 33, 34, 65 | SE: pp. 167–176<br>TE: pp. 45, 85<br>TR: Social Studies and Geography Skills, pp. 3, 4, 5, 6, 7, 10, 12, 13, 15, 16, 18, 19, 20, 21, 24, 25, 26, 27, 28, 29, 30, 31, 32, 33, 34, 35, 36, 37, 38, 39 | SE: pp. 106, 119, 122–123, 141, 191, 192<br>TE: pp. 20, 39, 113, 122–123, 213<br>TR: Social Studies and Geography Skills, pp. 3, 4, 5, 6, 7, 10, 12, 13, 15, 16, 18, 19, 20, 21, 24, 25, 26, 27, 28, 29, 30, 31, 32, 33, 34, 35, 36, 37, 38, 39 | SE: pp. 2–6, 17, 18, 23, 26–27, 39, 41<br>TE: pp. 4–7, 39, 89, 95<br>TR: Social Studies and Geography Skills, pp. 3, 4, 5, 6, 7, 10, 12, 13, 15, 16, 18, 19, 20, 21, 24, 25, 26, 27, 28, 29, 30, 31, 32, 33, 34, 35, 36, 37, 38, 39 | SE: pp. 2–7, 10, 14–19, 22, 23, 36, 40, 57, 137, 468, 493<br>TE: pp. 123, 127, 269, 520<br>TR: Social Studies and Geography Skills, pp. 1, 3, 6, 7, 17, 18, 23, 24, 25, 29, 31, 32, 35, 36 |
| SE: pp. 22, 188–190<br>TE: pp. 17, 25, 35, 57<br>TR: Social Studies and Geography Skills, pp. 3, 4, 5, 6, 7, 10, 12, 13, 15, 16, 18, 19, 20, 21, 24, 25, 26, 27, 28, 29, 30, 31, 32, 33, 34, 35, 36, 37, 38, 39 | SE: pp. 2–7, 18–19, 70<br>TE: pp. 41, 57, 113<br>TR: Social Studies and Geography Skills, pp. 3, 7, 10, 11, 25, 26, 31, 33, 34, 65 | SE: pp. 2–6, 174–176<br>TE: pp. 45, 85<br>TR: Social Studies and Geography Skills, pp. 3, 4, 5, 6, 7, 10, 12, 13, 15, 16, 18, 19, 20, 21, 24, 25, 26, 27, 28, 29, 30, 31, 32, 33, 34, 35, 36, 37, 38, 39 | SE: pp. 106, 119, 122–123, 141, 191, 192<br>TE: pp. 20, 39, 113, 122–123, 213<br>TR: Social Studies and Geography Skills, pp. 3, 4, 5, 6, 7, 10, 12, 13, 15, 16, 18, 19, 20, 21, 24, 25, 26, 27, 28, 29, 30, 31, 32, 33, 34, 35, 36, 37, 38, 39 | SE: pp. 2–6, 17, 18, 23, 26–27, 39, 41<br>TE: pp. 4–7, 39, 89, 95<br>TR: Social Studies and Geography Skills, pp. 3, 4, 5, 6, 7, 10, 12, 13, 15, 16, 18, 19, 20, 21, 24, 25, 26, 27, 28, 29, 30, 31, 32, 33, 34, 35, 36, 37, 38, 39 | SE: pp. 2–7, 23, 57, 137, 257, 276, 359, 365, 453, 473<br>TE: pp. 10, 123, 127, 269, 520<br>TR: Social Studies and Geography Skills, pp. 1, 3, 6, 7, 17, 18, 23, 24, 25, 29, 31, 32, 35, 36 |
| **Geographic Literacy, Test B** | | | | | |
| SE: pp. 22, 181–190<br>TE: pp. 17, 25, 35, 57<br>TR: Social Studies and Geography Skills, pp. 3, 4, 5, 6, 7, 10, 12, 13, 15, 16, 18, 19, 20, 21, 24, 25, 26, 27, 28, 29, 30, 31, 32, 33, 34, 35, 36, 37, 38, 39 | SE: pp. 2–7, 14–19, 70<br>TE: pp. 41, 57, 113<br>TR: Social Studies and Geography Skills, pp. 3, 7, 10, 11, 25, 26, 31, 33, 34, 65 | SE: pp. 167–176<br>TE: pp. 45, 85<br>TR: Social Studies and Geography Skills, pp. 3, 4, 5, 6, 7, 10, 12, 13, 15, 16, 18, 19, 20, 21, 24, 25, 26, 27, 28, 29, 30, 31, 32, 33, 34, 35, 36, 37, 38, 39 | SE: pp. 106, 119, 122–123, 141, 191, 192<br>TE: pp. 20, 39, 113, 122–123, 213<br>TR: Social Studies and Geography Skills, pp. 3, 4, 5, 6, 7, 10, 12, 13, 15, 16, 18, 19, 20, 21, 24, 25, 26, 27, 28, 29, 30, 31, 32, 33, 34, 35, 36, 37, 38, 39 | SE: pp. 2–6, 17, 18, 23, 26–27, 39, 41<br>TE: pp. 4–7, 39, 89, 95<br>TR: Social Studies and Geography Skills, pp. 3, 4, 5, 6, 7, 10, 12, 13, 15, 16, 18, 19, 20, 21, 24, 25, 26, 27, 28, 29, 30, 31, 32, 33, 34, 35, 36, 37, 38, 39 | SE: pp. 2–7, 10, 14–19, 22, 23, 36, 40, 57, 137, 468, 493<br>TE: pp. 123, 127, 269, 520<br>TR: Social Studies and Geography Skills, pp. 1, 3, 6, 7, 17, 18, 23, 24, 25, 29, 31, 32, 35, 36 |
| SE: pp. 22, 188–190<br>TE: pp. 17, 25, 35, 57<br>TR: Social Studies and Geography Skills, pp. 3, 4, 5, 6, 7, 10, 12, 13, 15, 16, 18, 19, 20, 21, 24, 25, 26, 27, 28, 29, 30, 31, 32, 33, 34, 35, 36, 37, 38, 39 | SE: pp. 2–7, 18–19, 70<br>TE: pp. 41, 57, 113<br>TR: Social Studies and Geography Skills, pp. 3, 7, 10, 11, 25, 26, 31, 33, 34, 65 | SE: pp. 2–6, 174–176<br>TE: pp. 45, 85<br>TR: Social Studies and Geography Skills, pp. 3, 4, 5, 6, 7, 10, 12, 13, 15, 16, 18, 19, 20, 21, 24, 25, 26, 27, 28, 29, 30, 31, 32, 33, 34, 35, 36, 37, 38, 39 | SE: pp. 106, 119, 122–123, 141, 191, 192<br>TE: pp. 20, 39, 113, 122–123, 213<br>TR: Social Studies and Geography Skills, pp. 3, 4, 5, 6, 7, 10, 12, 13, 15, 16, 18, 19, 20, 21, 24, 25, 26, 27, 28, 29, 30, 31, 32, 33, 34, 35, 36, 37, 38, 39 | SE: pp. 2–6, 17, 18, 23, 26–27, 39, 41<br>TE: pp. 4–7, 39, 89, 95<br>TR: Social Studies and Geography Skills, pp. 3, 4, 5, 6, 7, 10, 12, 13, 15, 16, 18, 19, 20, 21, 24, 25, 26, 27, 28, 29, 30, 31, 32, 33, 34, 35, 36, 37, 38, 39 | SE: pp. 2–7, 23, 57, 137, 257, 276, 359, 365, 453, 473<br>TE: pp. 10, 123, 127, 269, 520<br>TR: Social Studies and Geography Skills, pp. 1, 3, 6, 7, 17, 18, 23, 24, 25, 29, 31, 32, 35, 36 |

SE: Student Edition    TE: Teacher's Edition    TR: Teaching Resources    U: Unit Booklet

| Middle Grades Diagnostic Correlations (continued) | Test Item(s) | The American Nation, Survey | Civics: Participating in Government | World Explorer: Africa | World Explorer: The Ancient World | World Explorer: Asia and the Pacific |
|---|---|---|---|---|---|---|
| **Visual Analysis, Test A** | | | | | | |
| Analyzing Graphic Data | 1, 2, 3, 4, 5, 6, 7, 8, 9 | SE: pp. 71, 122, 154, 258, 271, 280, 410, 531, 603, 607, 712 TE: pp. 5, 148, 166D, 227, 253, 300D, 432D, 487, 503, 542D, 744D, 749 TR: U2, p. 53 | SE: pp. 6, 22, 29, 192, 364, 428 TE: pp. 316, 421, 507, 524 | SE: pp. 18, 55, 94, 100, 110, 122, 136, 149 TE: pp. 19, 137 TR: Social Studies and Geography Skills, pp. 53, 54 | SE: p. 20 TE: p. 21 TR: Social Studies and Geography Skills, p. 53 | SE: pp. 28, 46, 51, 97, 102, 128–129, 149 TE: p. 67 TR: Social Studies and Geography Skills, pp. 53, 54 |
| Analyzing Images | 1, 2, 3, 4 | SE: pp. 58, 209, 367, 436, 511, 528, 613, 644, 661, 822 TE: pp. 167, 247, 277, 359, 485, 543, 685, 773, 871 TR: U5, p. 22 U7, p. 5 | SE: pp. 84, 166, 448, 560 TE: pp. 463, 507 TR: Interpreting Political Cartoons booklet | SE: pp. 27, 44, 54, 65, 101, 117, 138, 152, 163, 172 TE: p. 1 TR: Social Studies and Geography Skills, p. 58 | SE: pp. 11, 21, 44, 47, 82, 102, 155, 136, 144 TE: pp. 1, 137 | SE: pp. 16, 33, 39, 68, 118, 137 TE: pp. 1, 125 |
| **Visual Analysis, Test B** | | | | | | |
| Analyzing Graphic Data | 1, 2, 3, 4, 5 | SE: pp. 71, 122, 154, 258, 271, 280, 410, 531, 603, 607, 712 TE: pp. 5, 148, 166D, 227, 253, 300D, 432D, 487, 503, 542D, 744D, 749 TR: U2, p. 53 | SE: pp. 6, 22, 29, 192, 364, 428 TE: pp. 316, 421, 507, 524 | SE: pp. 18, 55, 94, 100, 110, 122, 136, 149 TE: pp. 19, 137 TR: Social Studies and Geography Skills, pp. 53, 54 | SE: p. 20 TE: p. 21 TR: Social Studies and Geography Skills, p. 53 | SE: pp. 28, 46, 51, 97, 102, 128–129, 149 TE: p. 67 TR: Social Studies and Geography Skills, pp. 53, 54 |
| Analyzing Images | 6, 7, 8, 9, 10 | SE: pp. 58, 209, 367, 436, 511, 528, 613, 644, 661, 822 TE: pp. 167, 247, 277, 359, 485, 543, 685, 773, 871 TR: U5, p. 22 U7, p. 5 | SE: pp. 84, 166, 448, 560 TE: pp. 463, 507 TR: Interpreting Political Cartoons booklet | SE: pp. 27, 44, 54, 65, 101, 117, 138, 152, 163, 172 TE: p. 1 TR: Social Studies and Geography Skills, p. 58 | SE: pp. 11, 21, 44, 47, 82, 102, 155, 136, 144 TE: pp. 1, 137 | SE: pp. 16, 33, 39, 68, 118, 137 TE: pp. 1, 125 |

SE: Student Edition     TE: Teacher's Edition     TR: Teaching Resources     U: Unit Booklet

| World Explorer: Europe and Russia | World Explorer: Geography: Tools and Concepts | World Explorer: Latin America | World Explorer: Medieval Times to Today | World Explorer: United States and Canada | World Explorer: People, Places, and Cultures, National |
|---|---|---|---|---|---|
| **Visual Analysis, Test A** | | | | | |
| SE: pp. 17, 76, 98, 105, 115, 122, 128, 140, 147, 155, 162<br>TR: Social Studies and Geography Skills, p. 53 | SE: pp. 12, 48, 49, 62, 63, 68, 80, 90, 108, 109, 120<br>TE: p. 109<br>TR: Social Studies and Geography Skills, p. 54 | SE: pp. 7, 56, 65, 83, 84, 90, 97, 108, 114, 121, 122, 130, 133, 136, 143, 149, 151<br>TE: pp. 133, 149<br>TR: Social Studies and Geography Skills, p. 55 | SE: pp. 180–181<br>TE: pp. 109, 180–181<br>TR: Social Studies and Geography Skills, p. 54 | SE: pp. 7, 71, 76, 94, 100, 110–111<br>TE: pp. 71, 110–111, 129<br>TR: Social Studies and Geography Skills, p. 55 | SE: pp. 12, 37, 80, 90, 108–109, 120, 271, 228, 449, 457, 574<br>TE: pp. 32,131, 150, 239<br>TR: Social Studies and Geography Skills, pp. 51, 52, 53 |
| SE: pp. 13, 19, 26, 39, 49, 85, 90, 132, 160<br>TE: p. 1 | SE: pp. 9, 26, 36, 40, 54, 76, 80, 99, 104, 119, 120<br>TE: p. 1<br>TR: Social Studies and Geography Skills, pp. 58, 59 | SE: pp. 8, 12, 37, 40, 51, 62, 64, 75, 76, 91, 99, 112, 139, 152<br>TR: Social Studies and Geography Skills, p. 58 | SE: pp. 11, 33, 63<br>TE: p. 1<br>TR: Social Studies and Geography Skills, pp. 58, 59 | SE: pp. 22, 75<br>TE: pp. 1, 11<br>TR: Social Studies and Geography Skills, p. 58 | SE: pp. 9, 36, 76, 81, 133, 168, 209, 236, 358, 461<br>TE: p. 1<br>TR: Social Studies and Geography Skills, p. 57 |
| **Visual Analysis, Test B** | | | | | |
| SE: pp. 17, 76, 98, 105, 115, 122, 128, 140, 147, 155, 162<br>TR: Social Studies and Geography Skills, p. 53 | SE: pp. 12, 48, 49, 62, 63, 68, 80, 90, 108, 109, 120<br>TE: p. 109<br>TR: Social Studies and Geography Skills, p. 54 | SE: pp. 7, 56, 65, 83, 84, 90, 97, 108, 114, 121, 122, 130, 133, 136, 143, 149, 151<br>TE: pp. 133, 149<br>TR: Social Studies and Geography Skills, p. 55 | SE: pp. 180–181<br>TE: pp. 109, 180–181<br>TR: Social Studies and Geography Skills, p. 54 | SE: pp. 7, 71, 76, 94, 100, 110–111<br>TE: pp. 71, 110–111, 129<br>TR: Social Studies and Geography Skills, p. 55 | SE: pp. 12, 37, 80, 90, 108–109, 120, 271, 228, 449, 457, 574<br>TE: pp. 32,131, 150, 239<br>TR: Social Studies and Geography Skills, pp. 51, 52, 53 |
| SE: pp. 13, 19, 26, 39, 49, 85, 90, 132, 160<br>TE: p. 1 | SE: pp. 9, 26, 36, 40, 54, 76, 80, 99, 104, 119, 120<br>TE: p. 1<br>TR: Social Studies and Geography Skills, pp. 58, 59 | SE: pp. 8, 12, 37, 40, 51, 62, 64, 75, 76, 91, 99, 112, 139, 152<br>TR: Social Studies and Geography Skills, p. 58 | SE: pp. 11, 33, 63<br>TE: p. 1<br>TR: Social Studies and Geography Skills, pp. 58, 59 | SE: pp. 22, 75<br>TE: pp. 1, 11<br>TR: Social Studies and Geography Skills, p. 58 | SE: pp. 9, 36, 76, 81, 133, 168, 209, 236, 358, 461<br>TE: p. 1<br>TR: Social Studies and Geography Skills, p. 57 |

SE: Student Edition     TE: Teacher's Edition     TR: Teaching Resources     U: Unit Booklet

**TEST A—**
**GEOGRAPHIC LITERACY**

1. C
2. A
3. B
4. C
5. A
6. C
7. B
8. C
9. A
10. B
11. A
12. C
13. A
14. B
15. A
16. C

**TEST B—**
**GEOGRAPHIC LITERACY**

1. C
2. B
3. A
4. C
5. B
6. C
7. A
8. C
9. C
10. A
11. C
12. A
13. B
14. B
15. D
16. C
17. A

TEST A—
VISUAL ANALYSIS

1. B
2. A
3. C
4. D
5. B
6. B
7. D
8. C
9. D

TEST B—
VISUAL ANALYSIS

1. B
2. C
3. C
4. D
5. C
6. C
7. D
8. C
9. A
10. D

**TEST A—**
**CRITICAL**
**THINKING AND READING**

1. A
2. B
3. D
4. A
5. A
6. C
7. D
8. A
9. D
10. A
11. B
12. B
13. C
14. D
15. C
16. D
17. A
18. C
19. B
20. A

**TEST B—**
**CRITICAL**
**THINKING AND READING**

1. B
2. A
3. D
4. B
5. C
6. B
7. C
8. C
9. C
10. A
11. A
12. D
13. C
14. A
15. C
16. B

**TEST A—**
**COMMUNICATIONS**

1. B
2. D
3. B
4. A
5. B
6. C
7. B
8. B
9. D
10. D
11. B
12. C
13. B
14. C
15. B
16. C
17. B
18. C
19. C
20. D

**TEST B—**
**COMMUNICATIONS**

1. D
2. A
3. B
4. C
5. C
6. B
7. D
8. D
9. C
10. B
11. B
12. D
13. D
14. C
15. D
16. B
17. B
18. C
19. B
20. A